WORKING PAPERS
CHAPTERS 1-13

ACCOUNTING

WORKING PAPERS
CHAPTERS 1-13
Ellen Sweatt *Georgia Perimeter College*
William L. Sweatt, C.P.A.

ACCOUNTING
Sixth Edition

Charles T. Horngren
Walter T. Harrison
Linda S. Bamber

PEARSON
Prentice
Hall

Upper Saddle River, New Jersey 07458

VP/Editorial Director: Jeff Shelstad
Assistant Editor: Sam Goffinet
Manager, Print Production: Christy Mahon
Production Editor & Buyer: Carol O'Rourke
Printer/Binder: Courier, Stoughton

10 9 8 7 6 5 4 3 2 1
ISBN 0-13-143613-9

Contents

S1-2

S1-4

S1-6

S1-7

S1-9

S1-10

Gay Gillen eTravel

Income Statement

Month Ended April 30, 2005

Revenue:					5 5 0 0
Service Revenue					3 0 0 0
					8 5 0 0
Expenses:					
Lease Expense			4 0 0		
Rent Expense	1	1 0 0			
Salary Expense	1	2 0 0			
Utilities Expense		4 0 0		8 5 0 0	
	3	3 0 0		(3 3 0 0)	
Net Income				5 2 0 0	

Gay Gillen eTravel

Statement of Owner's Equity

Month Ended April 30, 2005

Gay Gillen, Capital, April 30, 2005		0
Add:		
Investments	3 0 0 0 0	
Net Income	5 2 0 0	
Subtract:	3 5 2 0 0	
Withdrawals	(2 0 0 0)	
Gay Gillen, Capital, April 30, 2005	3 3 2 0 0	

Gay Gillen eTravel

Balance Sheet

April 30, 2005

Assets							Liabilities						
Cash		1	9	9	0	0	Accounts Payable					2	0	0
Accounts Receivable			2	0	0	0							
Office Supplies				5	0	0	Owner's Equity						
Land		1	1	0	0	0	G.G. Capital			3	3	2	0	0
Total Assets		3	3	4	0	0				3	3	4	0	0

S1-13

Bellevard Auto Repair											
Income Statement											
Year Ended December 31, 2008											
Revenue:											
Service Revenue								1	0	1	0	0	0
Expenses:											
Insurance Expense		4	0	0	0						
Supplies Expense		1	0	0	0						
Fuel Expense		6	0	0	0						
Rent Expense		8	0	0	0						
Salary Expense	4	2	0	0	0						
	6	1	0	0	0						
						1	0	1	0	0	0
						(6	1	0	0	0)	
Net Income							4	0	0	0	0

Bellmead Auto Repair

Statement of Owner's Equity

Year Ended December 31, 2008

Capital – December 31, 2008 –		1	3	0	0	0
Add:					
Investments – 0					
Net Income – 40,000		4	0	0	0	0
Subtract:					
Owner Withdrawals – 36,000		(3	6	0	0	0)
		4	0	0	0

S1-15

Bellmead Auto Repair

Balance Sheet

December 31, 2008

Assets						Liabilities					
Cash	1	6	0	0	0	Accounts Payable		8	0	0	0
Accounts Receivable		7	0	0	0						
Supplies		2	0	0	0	Owner's Equity					
						Capital	1	7	0	0	0
Total Assets	2	5	0	0	0		2	5	0	0	0

E1-2

E1-4

E1-6

Req. 1

Req. 2

	1	2	3

Computations:

Chapter 1

Analysis of Transactions

DATE	ASSETS			=	LIABILITIES	+	OWNER'S EQUITY	TYPE OF OWNER'S EQUITY TRANSACTION
	Cash	Medical Supplies	Land		Accounts Payable		K. Luikhart (capital)	
July 6	60,000						60,000	Owner Investment
Balance	60,000	0	0		0		60,000	
July 9	(55,000)		55,000					
Balance	5,000	0	55,000		0		60,000	
July 12		2,000			2,000			
Balance	5,000	2,000	55,000		2,000		60,000	
July 15 *								
Balance	5,000	2,000	55,000		2,000		60,000	
July 15-31	7,000						7,000	Service Revenue
Balance	12,000	2,000	55,000		2,000		67,000	
July 15-31	(1,400)						(1,400)	Salary Expense
	(1,000)						(1,000)	Rent Expense
	(300)						(300)	Utilities Expense
Balance	9,300	1,000	55,000		2,000		64,300	
July 28	500	(500)						
Balance	9,800	1,500	55,000		2,000		64,300	
July 31	(1,500)				(1,500)			
Balance	8,300	1,500	55,000		500		64,300	
Total	64,800				64,800			

Req. 1

Req. 2

Req. 1

Req. 2

			J.D.'s Graphic Design											
			Balance Sheet											
			November 30, 2009											
Assets							Liabilities							
Cash			2 0 0 0				Accounts Payable					2 5 0 0		
Accounts Receivable			6 9 0 0				Note Payable					8 0 0 0		
Supplies			6 0 0											
Office Equipment			1 5 5 0 0				Owner's Equity							
							J.D. Power Capital					1 4 5 0 0		
Total Assets			2 5 0 0 0									2 5 0 0 0		

Req. 1

Award Specialties				
Income Statement				
Year Ended December 31, 2006				
Revenue:				
Service Revenue				161 200
Expense:				
Utilities Expense		6 800		
Supplies Expense		4 000		
Rent Expense		24 000		
Salary Expense		60 000		
Property Tax Expense		1 200		
		96 000		161 200
				(96 000)
Net Income				65 200

Req. 2

Computations:

Req. 1

Req. 2

P1-1A

Lynn Greenspan, Attorney

Chapter 1

Analysis of Transactions

Req. 1

* = Personal account – Does not affect business

DATE		ASSETS			=	LIABILITIES	+	OWNER'S EQUITY	TYPE OF OWNER'S EQUITY TRANSACTION
	Cash	Accounts Receivable	Supplies	Office Furniture		Accounts Payable		Lynn Greenspan (Capital)	
July 1 *									
July 2 *									
July 3 *									
July 5 *	$100,000							$100,000	
July 6 *									
July 7	-$500	0	$500						
Balance	$99,500	0	$500	0		0		$100,000	
July 9		0	$500	$9,500		$9,500			
Balance	$99,500	0	$500	$9,500		$9,500		$100,000	
July 13		$3,000	$500	$9,500		$9,500		$3,000	Revenue
Balance	$99,500	$3,000	$500	$9,500		$9,500		$103,000	
July 20	-$1,900	$3,000	$500	$9,500		$9,500		-$1,900	Expense
Balance	$97,600	$3,000	$500	$9,500		$9,500		$104,100	
July 31	-$10,000	$3,000	$500	$9,500		$9,500		-$10,000	Owner withdrawal
Balance	$87,600	$3,000	$500	$9,500		$9,500		$91,100	
Total	$100,600 (Add all 4 up)	Add all 4 up				$60,600		Add 7 up	

Req. 2

A. Total Assests = $100,600

B. Total Liabilities = $9,500

C. Total Owner's Equity = $91,100

D. Net income = Total Revenue - Total Expenses

= $3,000 - $1,900 = $1,100

Analysis of Transactions

Req. 1

Subtract - ( )

DATE	ASSETS				= LIABILITIES	+ OWNER'S EQUITY	TYPE OF OWNER'S EQUITY TRANSACTION
	Cash	Accounts Receivable	Supplies	Land	Accounts Payable	Daniel Peavy Capital	
Balance	$1,770	$3,240	$0	$24,100	$5,400	$23,660	
A.	$12,000					$12,000	Owner Investment
Balance	$13,720	$3,240	$0	$24,100	$5,400	$35,660	
B.	-$5,400				-$5,400		
Balance	$8,320	$3,240	$0	$24,100	$0	$35,660	
C.	$1,100					$1,100	Service Revenue
Balance	$9,420	$3,240	$0	$24,100	$0	$36,760	
D.	$750	-$750					
Balance	$10,170	$2,490	$0	$24,100	$0	$36,760	
E.			$720		$720		
Balance	$10,170	$2,490	$720	$24,100	$720	$36,760	
F.		$5,000				$5,000	Service Revenue
Balance	$10,170	$7,490	$720	$24,100	$720	$41,760	
G.	$1,700					$1,700	Owner Investment
Balance	$11,870	$7,490	$720	$24,100	$720	$43,460	
H.	-$1,200					-$1,200	Rent Expense
I.	-$660					-$660	Advertising Expense
Balance	$10,010	$7,490	$720	$24,100	$720	$41,600	
J.	$80		-$80				
Balance	$10,090	$7,490	$640	$24,100	$720	$41,600	
J.	-$4,000					-$4,000	Owner Withdrawal
Balance	$6,090	$7,490	$640	$24,100	$720	$37,600	
Total	$38,320				$58,320		

Req. 2

Peavy Design				
Income Statement				
Month ended May 31, 2005				
Total Revenue :				
Service Revenue (1,100 + 5,000)				6 1 0 0
Expenses :				
Rent Expense (1,200)		1 2 0 0		
Advertising Expense (660)		6 6 0		
Total Expenses				1 8 6 0
Net Income - 4240				
				4 2 4 0

Req. 3

Peavy Design		
Statement of Owner's Equity		
Month ended May 31, 2005		
Capital - April 30, 2005 - $23,460		2 3 4 6 0
Add :		
Investments - 12,000 + 1,700		1 3 7 0 0
Net Income for the month - $4,240		4 2 4 0
Subtract :		1 3 7 0 0
Owner Withdrawals - $4,000		(4 0 0 0)
Net Loss - 0		
Capital Balance May 31, 2005		3 7 6 0 0

Req. 4

	Peavy Design						
	Balance Sheet						
	May 31, 2005						
Assets				**Liabilities:**			
Cash		6 0 9 0		Accounts Payable			7 2 0
Accounts Receivable		7 4 9 0		**Owner's Equity:**			
Supplies		6 4 0		D.P. Capital		3 7 6 0 0
Land	2 4 1 0 0						
Total Assets	3 8 3 2 0			Total		3 8 3 2 0	

Collins Photographic Studio

Income Statement

Year Ended December 31, 2009

Revenue:									
Service Revenue						7 0 0 0 0			
Expense:									
Salary Expense	2 2 0 0 0								
Rent Expense	7 0 0 0								
Advertising Expense	4 0 0 0								
	3 3 0 0 0								
					7 0 0 0 0				
					(3 3 0 0 0)				
Net Income						3 7 0 0 0			

Collins Photographic Studio

Statement of Owner's Equity

Year Ended December 31, 2009

Capital – December 31, 2008		5 0 0 0 0		
Add:				
Investments				
Net Income		3 7 0 0 0		
Subtract:				
Owner withdrawals		(1 6 0 0 0)		
Net Loss				
Capital Balance December 31, 2009		7 1 0 0 0		

				Collins Photographic Studio											
				Balance Sheet											
				December 31, 2009											
Assets						Liabilities									
Cash		1	6	0	0	0	Accounts Payable					6	0	0	0
Accounts Receivable			8	0	0	0	Note Payable				1	2	0	0	0
Equipment		6	5	0	0	0									
							Owner's Equity								
							L. Collins Capital				7	1	0	0	0
Total Assets		8	9	0	0	0					8	9	0	0	0

Req. 1

Vail Financial Consultants
Income Statement
Year Ended Dec. 31, 2004

Revenue:			
Service Revenue			108 000
Expenses:			
Interest Expense	4 000		
Property Tax Expense	2 000		
Rent Expense	14 000		
Salary Expense	38 000		
Utilities Expense	3 000		
Total Expenses	61 000		
			108 000
			(61 000)
Net Income 47,000			47 000

Req. 2

Vail Financial Consultants
Statement of Owner's Equity
Year Ended Dec. 31, 2004

M.V. Capital, Dec. 31, 2003		43 000
Add:		
Net Income – 47,000		47 000
Investments – 0		90 000
Subtract:		
Owner Withdrawal – 32,000		(32 000)
M.V. Capital, Dec. 31, 2004		58 000

Req. 3

	Vail Financial Consultants											
	Balance Sheet											
	Dec. 31, 2004											
Assets							Liabilities :					
Cash		7	0	0	0		Accounts Payable		1	2	0	0	0
Accounts Receivable		3	0	0	0		Note Payable		3	1	0	0	0
Supplies		7	0	0	0		Interest Payable			1	0	0	0
Equipment	2	1	0	0	0		Total Liabilities		4	4	0	0	0
Buildings	5	6	0	0	0								
Land		8	0	0	0		Owner's Equity :						
							M.V. Capital		5	8	0	0	0
Total Assets	1	0	2	0	0	0		1	0	2	0	0	0

Req. 4

A. Profit - $47,000 (Net Income)

B. The owner increased the company's capital, because profit was $47,000 and the owner only withdrew $32,000.

C. Total economic resources = Assets = $102,000

Total amount the company owes = Liabilities = $44,000

Owner's equity ($102,000 - $44,000) = $58,000

Req. 1

Req. 2

Req. 2

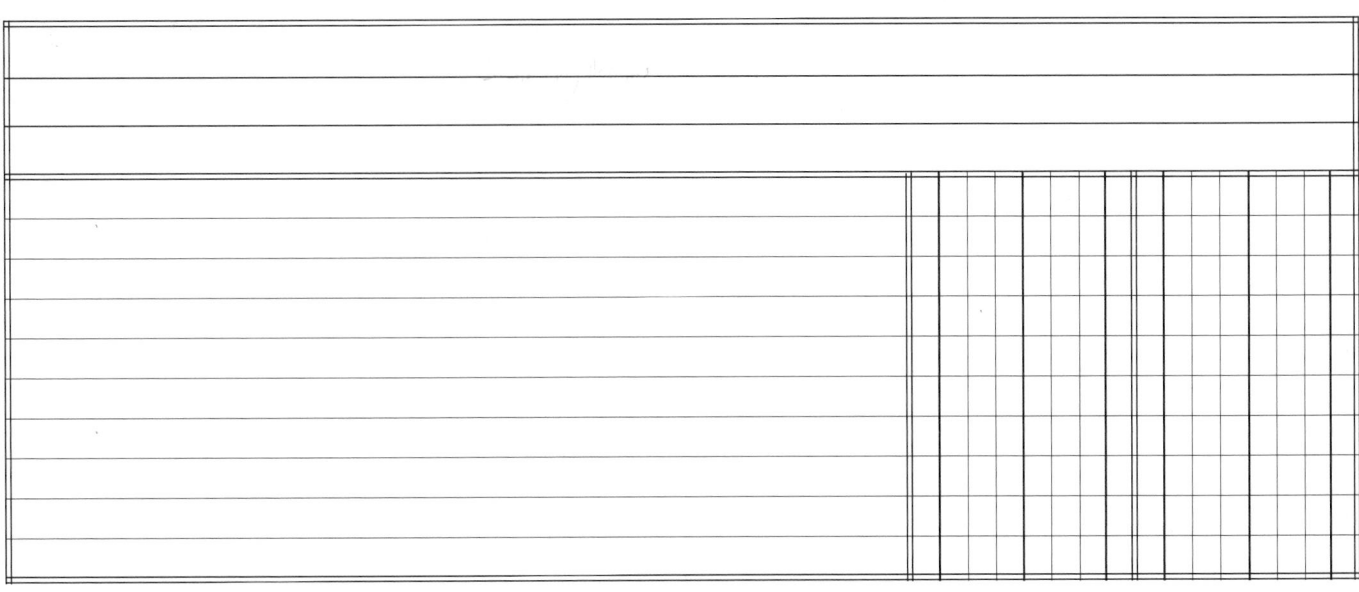

Req. 3

Req. 4

a.

Robinson Chauffeur Service										
Income Statement										
Year Ended December 31, 2005										
Revenue:										
Service Revenue								6 6 0 0 0		
Expense:										
Salary Expense		1 4 0 0 0								
Insurance Expense		4 0 0 0								
Advertising Expense		2 0 0 0								
		2 0 0 0 0								
								6 6 0 0 0		
								(2 0 0 0 0)		
Net Income								4 6 0 0 0		

b.

Robinson Chauffeur Service					
Statement of Owner's Equity					
Year Ended December 31, 2005					
Capital - December 31, 2004		5 6 0 0 0			
Add:					
Net Income		4 6 0 0 0			
Subtract					
Owner Withdrawal		(5 0 0 0 0)			
J.R Capital December 31, 2005		5 2 0 0 0			

Req. 1

						Epson Printing Co.						
						Balance sheet						
						Month Ended July 31, 2003						
Assets						Liabilities						
Cash	1	2	0	0	0	Accounts Payable			9	0	0	0
Office Supplies		1	0	0	0	Note Payable	3	6	0	0	0
Land	4	4	0	0	0						
Office Furniture		8	0	0	0	Owner's Equity						
Accounts Receivable	2	3	0	0	0	Capital		4	3	0	0	0
Total Assets	8	8	0	0	0			8	8	0	0	0

Req. 2

Req. 1

NAME
SECTION
DATE

Chapter 1

Decision Case 1
(Continued)

Req. 2

Reqs. 1 & 2

NAME
SECTION
DATE
Reqs. 1 & 2

Chapter 1

Ethical Issue 1

Ethical Issue 2

Chapter 1

Project 1

Team Projects

Req. 1

Req. 2 (Transactions)

Req. 3

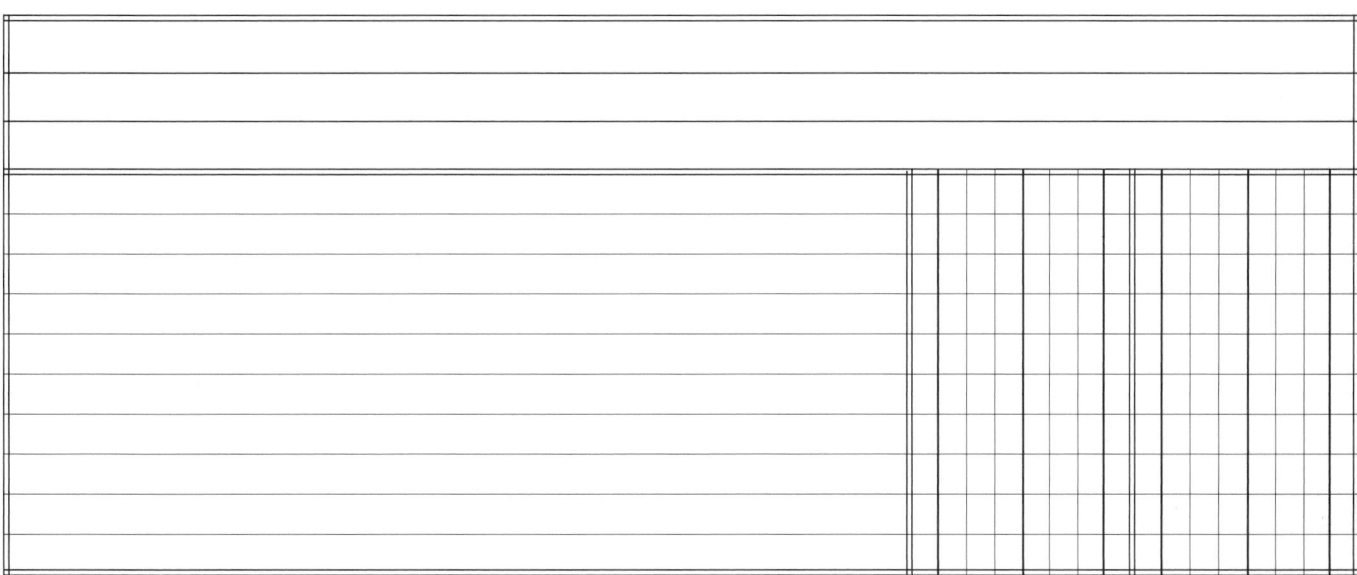

Req. 3

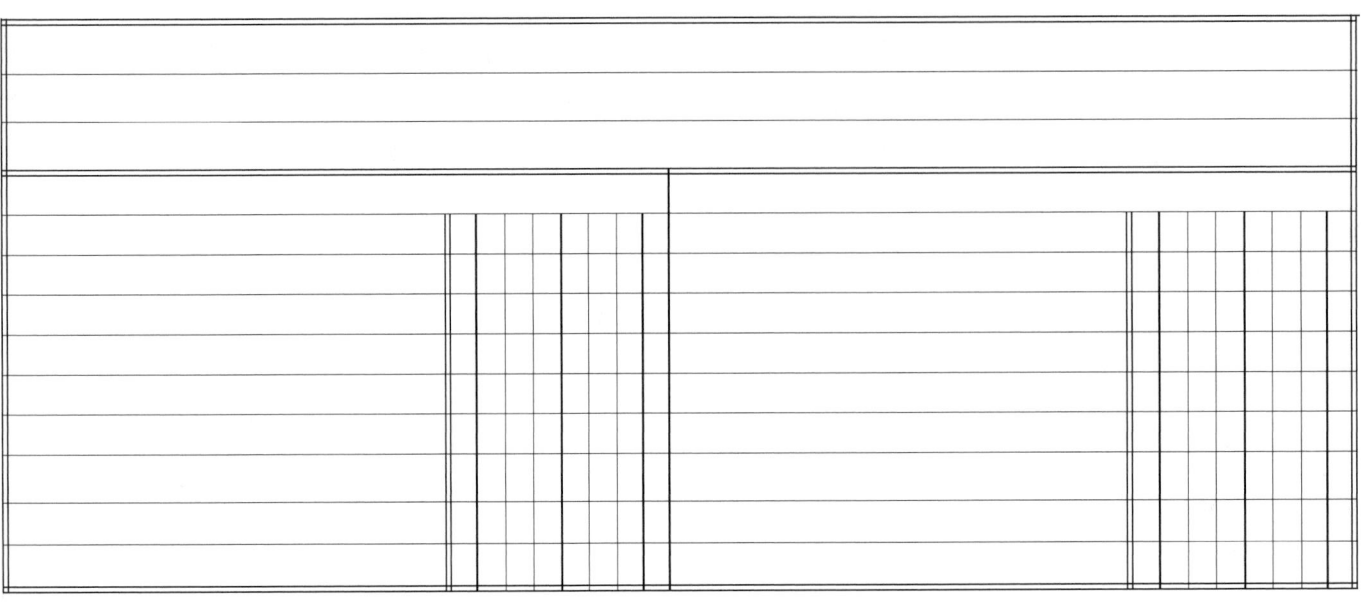

Req. 4

Req. 1

Req. 2

Req. 3

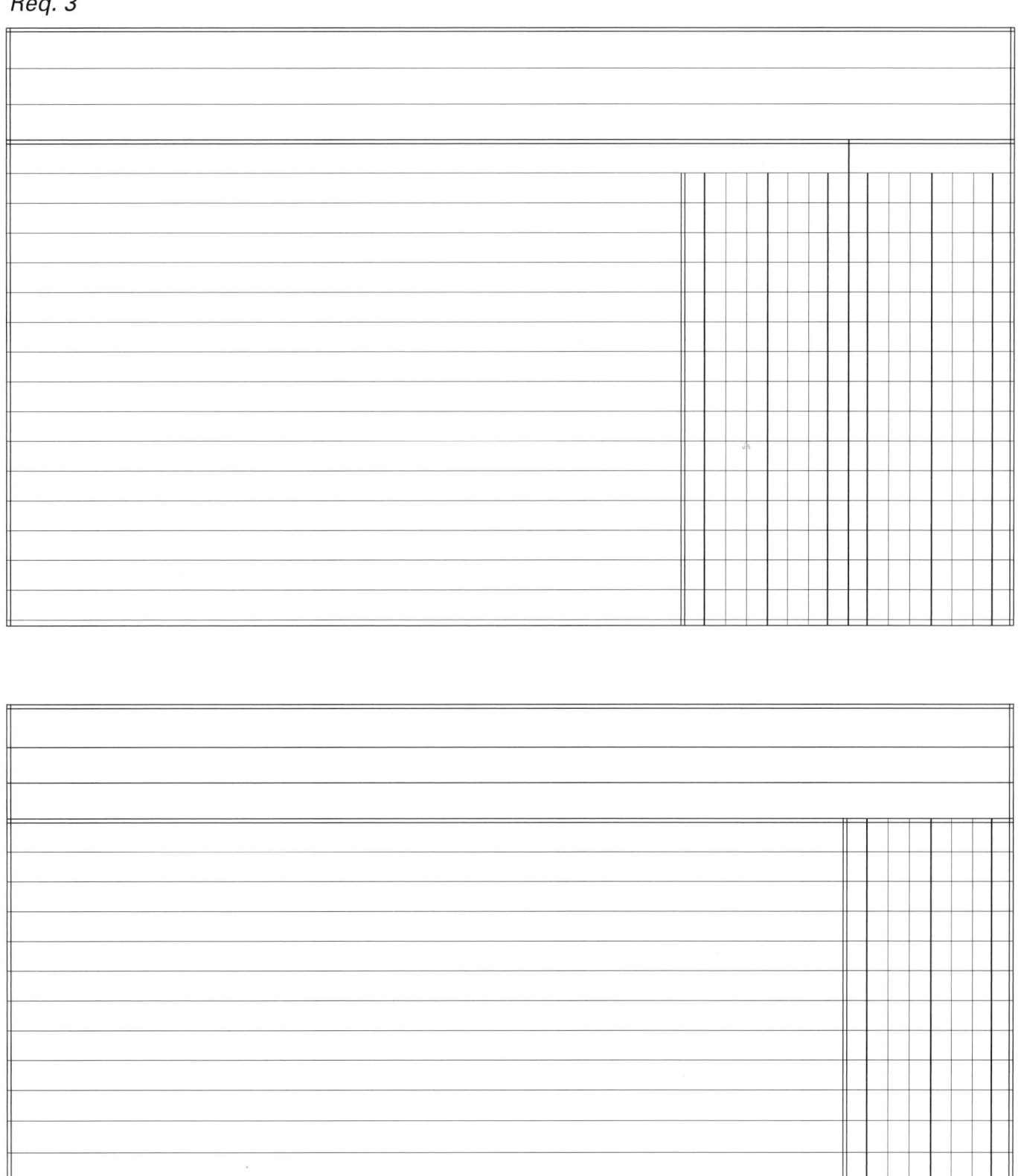

Req. 3 - Continued

Req. 4

Journal

DATE		ACCOUNTS AND EXPLANATIONS	POST. REF.	DEBIT	CREDIT
Sept.	1	Cash (↑ asset; debit)		30000	
		Liana Garcia, Capital (↑ equity; credit)			30000
		Investment by owner			
Sept.	2	Medical Supplies (↑ assets; debit)		10000	
		Account Payable (↑ liabilities; credit)			10000
		Purchased medical supplies on account			
Sept.	2	Rent Expense (↑ expense; debit)		4000	
		Cash (↓ asset; credit)			4000
		Paid rent			
Sept.	3				
		Cash (↑ asset; debit)		2000	
		Service Revenue (↑ revenue; credit)			2000

P2-7A
?

Req. 1

		Journal				
DATE		ACCOUNTS AND EXPLANATIONS	POST. REF.	DEBIT	CREDIT	

Req. 2

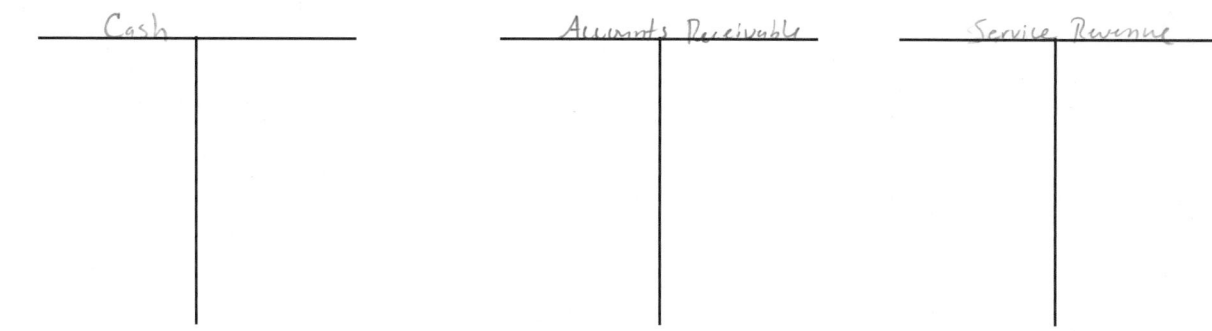

Cash   Accounts Receivable   Service Revenue

Req. 3

Reqs. 1 & 2

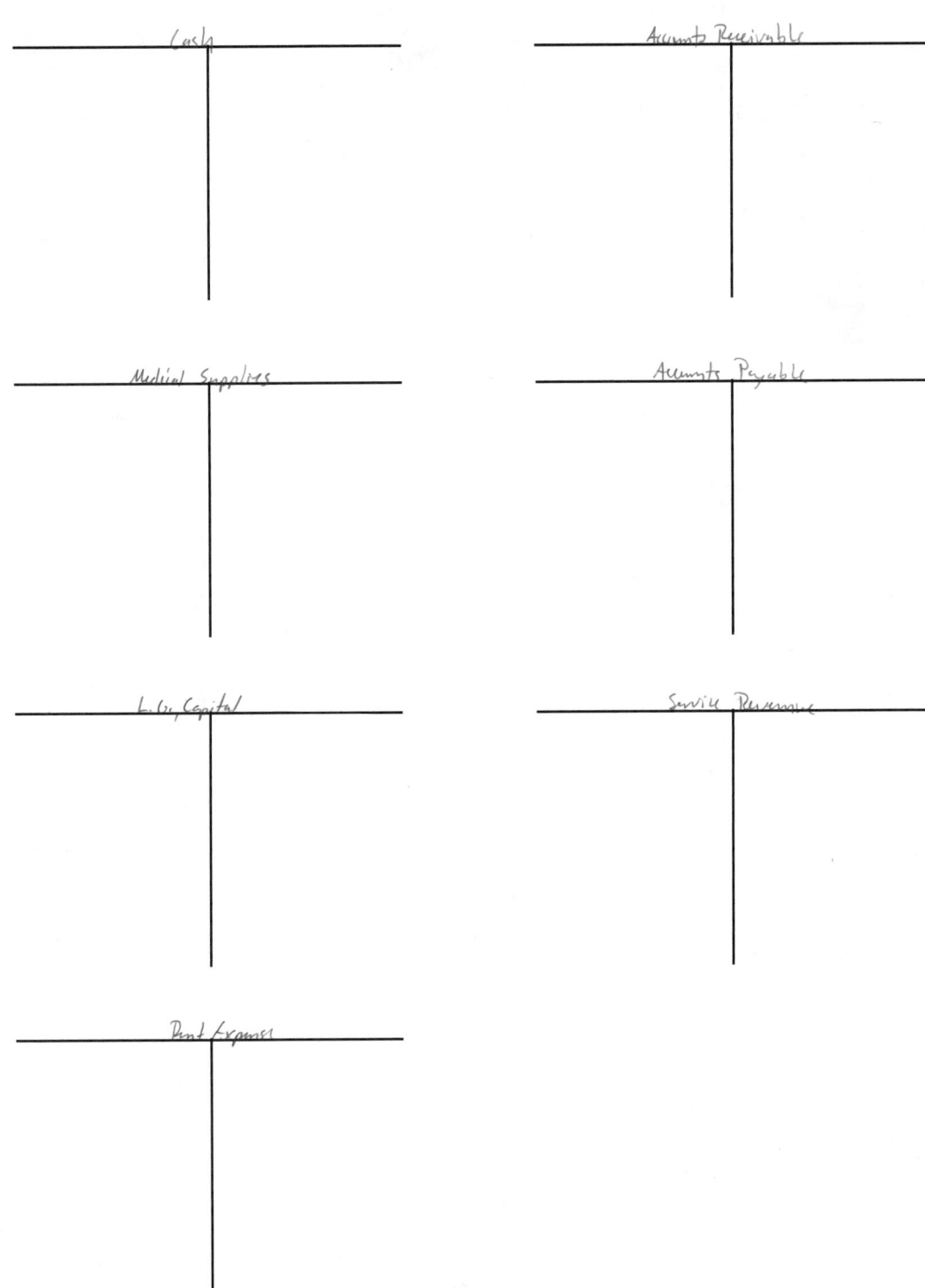

Req. 3

ACCOUNT	DEBIT	CREDIT

	MILLIONS	
ACCOUNT	DEBIT	CREDIT

ACCOUNT	DEBIT	CREDIT

ACCOUNT	DEBIT	CREDIT

Reqs. 1–3

Journal

DATE		ACCOUNTS AND EXPLANATIONS	POST. REF.	DEBIT	CREDIT
Dec.	1	Interest Expense	✓	500	
		Cash	✓		500
Dec.	5	Office Furniture	✓	800	
		Accounts Payable	✓		800
Dec.	10	Accounts Receivable	✓	1600	
		Service Revenue	✓		1600
Dec.	12	Cash	✓	7000	
		Note Payable	✓		7000
Dec.	19	Cash	✓	29000	
		Land	✓		29000
Dec.	21	Building	✓	140000	
		Note Payable	✓		140000
Dec.	27	Accounts Payable	✓	800	
		Cash	✓		800

Req. 1

Cash

70,000 – March 1	60,000 – March 4
3,000 – March 6	100 – March 9
1,200 – March 23	1,700 – March 31
74,200	61,800

Balance 12,400

Accounts Receivable

| 1,600 – March 17 | 1,200 – March 23 |

Balance 400

Supplies

| 200 – March 2 | |

Balance 200

Building

| 60,000 – March 4 | |

Balance 60,000

Accounts Payable

| 100 – March 9 | 200 – March 2 |

Balance 100

R.H., Capital

| | 70,000 – March 1 |

Balance 70,000

Service Revenue

| | 3,000 – March 6 |
| | 1,600 – March 17 |

Balance 4,600

Salary Expense

| 1,200 – March 31 | |

Balance 1,200

Rent Expense

| 500 – March 31 | |

Balance 500

Req. 2

ACCOUNT	DEBIT	CREDIT
Westview Landscaping		
Trial Balance		
March 31, 2008		
Cash	12400	
Accounts Receivable	400	
Supplies	200	
Building	60000	
Accounts Payable	73000	600
J.H., Capital		20000
Service Revenue		4600
Salary Expense	1200	74700
Rent Expense	500	
	1700	
Total	74700	74700

E2-7

Req. 1

Reqs. 2 & 3

Req. 4

ACCOUNT	DEBIT	CREDIT

Journal

DATE	ACCOUNTS AND EXPLANATIONS	POST. REF.	DEBIT	CREDIT

ACCOUNT	DEBIT	CREDIT

ACCOUNT	DEBIT	CREDIT

ACCOUNT	DEBIT	CREDIT

ACCOUNT	DEBIT	CREDIT

Reqs. 1 & 2

Req. 3

Chapter 2

E2-15

EFFECT ON TRIAL BALANCE

ACCOUNT(S) MISSTATED

RELEVANT JOURNAL ENTRIES

a. _____

b. _____

c. _____

d. _____

Reqs. 1 & 3

Req. 2

		Journal			
DATE		ACCOUNTS AND EXPLANATIONS	POST. REF.	DEBIT	CREDIT

Req. 4

ACCOUNT	DEBIT	CREDIT

Req. 1

_____

_____

_____

_____

_____

_____

_____

_____

Req. 2

General Journal			
DATE	ACCOUNTS AND EXPLANATIONS	POST. REF.	DEBIT	CREDIT

Req. 3

Req. 4

		Journal								
DATE		**ACCOUNTS AND EXPLANATIONS**	**POST. REF.**		**DEBIT**			**CREDIT**		
June	1	Cash (↑ asset; debit)			5 5 0 0 0					
		Art Levitt, Capital (↑ equity; credit)						5 5 0 0 0	
		Received an investment from the owner								
June	5	Rent Expense (↑ expense; debit)			7 0 0					
		Cash (↓ asset; credit)						7 0 0		
		Paid Rent Expense								
June	9	Land (↑ asset; debit)			2 2 0 0 0					
		Cash (↓ asset; credit)						2 2 0 0 0	
		Purchased land								
June	10	Supplies (↑ asset; debit)			1 2 0 0					
		Accounts Payable (↑ liabilities; credit)						1 2 0 0	
		Purchased supplies on account								
June	19	Cash (↑ asset; debit)			2 0 0 0 0					
		Note Payable (↑ liability; credit)						2 0 0 0 0	
		Borrowed cash on a note payable								
June	22	Accounts Payable (↓ liability; debit)			1 0 0 0					
		Cash (↓ asset; credit)						1 0 0 0	
		Paid on account								
June	30	Cash (↑ asset; debit)			6 0 0 0					
		Service Revenue (↑ equity; credit)						6 0 0 0	
		Accounts Receivable (↑ asset; debit)			5 0 0 0					
		Service Revenue (↑ revenue; credit)						5 0 0 0	
June	30	Salary Expense (↑ expense; debit)			2 4 0 0					
		Rent Expense (↑ expense; debit)			1 5 0 0					
		Utilities Expense (↑ expense; debit)		+	4 0 0					
		Cash (↓ asset; credit)						4 3 0 0	
June	30	Art Levitt, Withdrawals (O.E.) (↓ equity; debit)			1 0 0 0 0					
		Cash (↓ asset; credit)						1 0 0 0 0	

Req. 1

	Journal				
DATE	ACCOUNTS AND EXPLANATIONS	POST. REF.	DEBIT	CREDIT	

Req. 1 (Continued)

Journal

DATE	ACCOUNTS AND EXPLANATIONS	POST. REF.	DEBIT	CREDIT

Req. 2

Req. 3

ACCOUNT	DEBIT	CREDIT

Req. 1

Page 6

Journal

DATE		ACCOUNTS AND EXPLANATIONS	POST. REF.	DEBIT	CREDIT
Nov.	16	Cash	11	6 0 0 0	
		Accounts Receivable	12		6 0 0 0
Nov.	17	Accounts Receivable	12	1 7 0 0	
		Service Revenue	41		1 7 0 0
Nov.	21	Not a business transaction			
		Personal Transaction			
Nov.	22	Supplies	13	8 0 0	
		Accounts Payable	21		8 0 0
Nov.	23	L. Q. Withdraw	32	2 1 0 0	
		Cash	11		2 1 0 0
Nov.	23	Accounts Payable	21	2 6 0 0	
		Cash	11		2 6 0 0
Nov.	24	Cash	11	1 9 0 0	
		Service Revenue	41		1 9 0 0
Nov.	30	Rent Expense	52	7 0 0	
		Cash	11		7 0 0
Nov.	30	Salary Expense	51	2 1 0 0	
		Cash	11		2 1 0 0

Req. 2

ACCOUNT	Cash								ACCOUNT NO. 11	
		JRNL. REF.		DEBIT		CREDIT		BALANCE		
DATE	ITEM							DEBIT		CREDIT
Nov. 15	Balance	✓						3000		
Nov. 16		J6		6000				9000		
Nov. 23		J6				2100		6900		
Nov. 23		J6				2600		4300		
Nov. 24		J6		1900				6200		
Nov. 30		J6				700		5500		
Nov. 30		J6				2100		3400		

ACCOUNT	Accounts Receivable								ACCOUNT NO. 12	
		JRNL. REF.		DEBIT		CREDIT		BALANCE		
DATE	ITEM							DEBIT		CREDIT
Nov. 15	Balance	✓						8000		
Nov. 16		J6				6000		2000		
Nov. 17		J6		1700				3700		

ACCOUNT	Supplies								ACCOUNT NO. 13	
		JRNL. REF.		DEBIT		CREDIT		BALANCE		
DATE	ITEM							DEBIT		CREDIT
Nov. 15	Balance	✓						600		
Nov. 22		J6		800				1400		

Req. 2 (Continued)

ACCOUNT	Equipment						ACCOUNT NO. 14		
		JRNL.					**BALANCE**		
DATE	ITEM	REF.	DEBIT	CREDIT			DEBIT	CREDIT	
Nov. 15	Balance	✓					1 5 0 0 0		

ACCOUNT	Accounts Payable						ACCOUNT NO. 21		
		JRNL.					**BALANCE**		
DATE	ITEM	REF.	DEBIT	CREDIT			DEBIT	CREDIT	
Nov. 15	Balance	✓						4 4 0 0	
Nov. 22		J6		8 0 0				5 4 0 0	
Nov. 23		J6	2 4 0 0					2 8 0 0	

ACCOUNT	Robert Quiroga, Capital						ACCOUNT NO. 31		
		JRNL.					**BALANCE**		
DATE	ITEM	REF.	DEBIT	CREDIT			DEBIT	CREDIT	
Nov. 15	Balance	✓						2 0 0 0 0	

ACCOUNT	Robert Quiroga, Withdrawal						ACCOUNT NO. 32		
		JRNL.					**BALANCE**		
DATE	ITEM	REF.	DEBIT	CREDIT			DEBIT	CREDIT	
Nov. 15	Balance	✓					2 3 0 0		
Nov. 23		J6	2 1 0 0				4 4 0 0		

ACCOUNT	Service Revenue						ACCOUNT NO. 41		
		JRNL.					**BALANCE**		
DATE	ITEM	REF.	DEBIT	CREDIT			DEBIT	CREDIT	
Nov. 15	Balance	✓						7 1 0 0	
Nov. 17		J6		1 7 0 0				8 8 0 0	
Nov. 24		J6		1 9 0 0				1 0 7 0 0	

Req. 2 (Continued)

ACCOUNT	Salary Expense							ACCOUNT NO.	51	
		JRNL. REF.						BALANCE		
DATE	ITEM		DEBIT		CREDIT			DEBIT		CREDIT
Nov. 15	Balance	✓						1 8 0 0		
Nov. 30		JL	2 1 0 0					3 9 0 0		

ACCOUNT	Rent Expense							ACCOUNT NO.	52	
		JRNL. REF.						BALANCE		
DATE	ITEM		DEBIT		CREDIT			DEBIT		CREDIT
Nov. 15	Balance	✓						1 0 0 0		
Nov. 30		JL	7 0 0					1 7 0 0		

Req. 3

	Robert Quiroga, Registered Dietician			
	Trial Balance			
	Nov. 30, 2003			
Acct. No.	**ACCOUNT**	**DEBIT**	**CREDIT**	
11	Cash	3400		
12	Account Receivable	3700	600	
13	Supplies	1400		
14	Equipment	1500		
21	Accounts Payable		2800	
31	R.Q., Capital		20000	
32	R.Q., Withdrawals	4400		
41	Service Revenue		10700	
51	Salary Expense	3900		
52	Rent Expense	1700		
	Total	33500	33500	

Total Revenues - Total Expenses

Req. 1

ACCOUNT	DEBIT	CREDIT
Online Cable Service		
Trial Balance		
March 31, 2001		
Cash	6 6 0 0	
Accounts Receivable	2 5 4 0	
Supplies	6 0 0	
Office Furniture	2 1 3 0 0	
Computers	4 6 0 0 0	
Accounts Payable		2 8 0 0
Note Payable		1 8 3 0 0
Meredith Ballard, Capital		5 0 8 0 0
Meredith Ballard, Withdrawals	5 0 0 0	
Service Revenue		1 3 2 0 0
Salary Expense	1 3 0 0	
Rent Expense	1 2 0 0	
Advertising Expense	3 0 0	
Utilities Expense	2 6 0	
Total	8 5 1 0 0	8 5 1 0 0

Cash - 6,200 + 400 = 6,600

Rent - 500 + 700 (500 + 350 + 350) Had a -350 have to add 350 + 500 = 1200

Service Revenue - 4,900 + 8,300 = 13,200

Accounts Receivable - 600 - 60 = 540   2,000 + 540 = 2,540

Utilities Expense - 200 + 60 = 260

Supplies - 500 + 100 = 600

Accounts Payable - 2,700 + 100 = 2,800

Req. 2

Online Cable Service						
Income Statement						
March 31, 2001						
Revenues:						
Service Revenue					1 3 2 0 0
Expenses:						
Salary Expense		1 3 0 0			
Rent Expense		1 2 0 0			
Advertising Expense		3 0 0			
Utilities Expense		2 6 0			
		3 0 6 0			
Net Income		3 0 6 0		1 0 1 4 0

Reqs. 1 & 2

Reqs. 1 & 2 (Continued)

Req. 3

ACCOUNT	DEBIT	CREDIT

Req. 1

_____
_____
_____
_____
_____
_____
_____
_____

Req. 2

			Journal			
DATE		ACCOUNTS AND EXPLANATIONS	POST. REF.	DEBIT	CREDIT	

_____
_____
_____
_____

Req. 1

		Journal			
DATE		ACCOUNTS AND EXPLANATIONS	POST. REF.	DEBIT	CREDIT

Req. 1 (Continued)

		Journal			
DATE		ACCOUNTS AND EXPLANATIONS	POST. REF.	DEBIT	CREDIT

Req. 2

Req. 3

ACCOUNT	DEBIT	CREDIT

Req. 1

		Journal			
DATE		ACCOUNTS AND EXPLANATIONS	POST. REF.	DEBIT	CREDIT

Req. 2

ACCOUNT					ACCOUNT NO.	
		JRNL.			BALANCE	
DATE	ITEM	REF.	DEBIT	CREDIT	DEBIT	CREDIT

ACCOUNT					ACCOUNT NO.	
		JRNL.			BALANCE	
DATE	ITEM	REF.	DEBIT	CREDIT	DEBIT	CREDIT

Req. 2 (Continued)

ACCOUNT					ACCOUNT NO.		
DATE	ITEM	JRNL. REF.	DEBIT	CREDIT	BALANCE DEBIT	CREDIT	

ACCOUNT					ACCOUNT NO.		
DATE	ITEM	JRNL. REF.	DEBIT	CREDIT	BALANCE DEBIT	CREDIT	

ACCOUNT					ACCOUNT NO.		
DATE	ITEM	JRNL. REF.	DEBIT	CREDIT	BALANCE DEBIT	CREDIT	

ACCOUNT					ACCOUNT NO.		
DATE	ITEM	JRNL. REF.	DEBIT	CREDIT	BALANCE DEBIT	CREDIT	

ACCOUNT					ACCOUNT NO.		
DATE	ITEM	JRNL. REF.	DEBIT	CREDIT	BALANCE DEBIT	CREDIT	

Req. 2 (Continued)

ACCOUNT					ACCOUNT NO.		
		JRNL.			BALANCE		
DATE	ITEM	REF.	DEBIT	CREDIT	DEBIT	CREDIT	

ACCOUNT					ACCOUNT NO.		
		JRNL.			BALANCE		
DATE	ITEM	REF.	DEBIT	CREDIT	DEBIT	CREDIT	

ACCOUNT					ACCOUNT NO.		
		JRNL.			BALANCE		
DATE	ITEM	REF.	DEBIT	CREDIT	DEBIT	CREDIT	

Req. 3

ACCOUNT	DEBIT	CREDIT

Req. 1

ACCOUNT	DEBIT	CREDIT

Req. 2

Reqs. 1 & 2

Reqs. 1 & 2 (Continued)

Req. 3

ACCOUNT	DEBIT	CREDIT

Req. 1

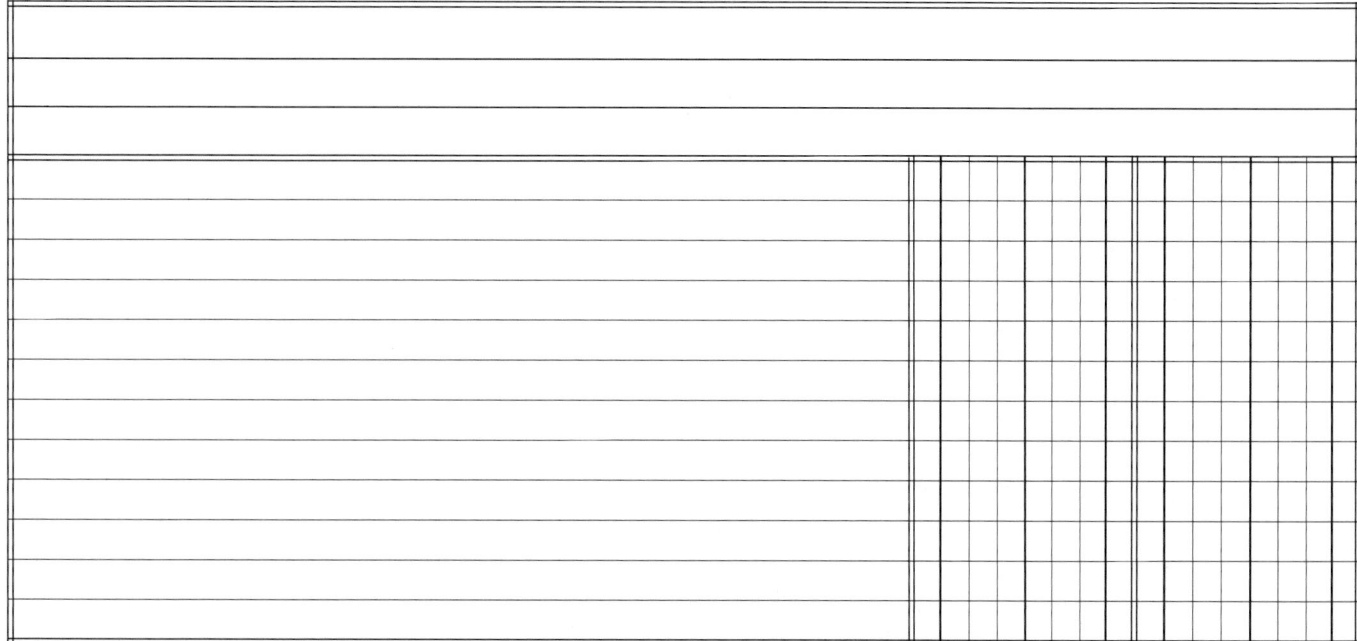

Req. 2

Req. 3

Reqs. 1 & 2

NAME
SECTION
DATE

Chapter 2

Decision Case 1

(Continued)

Req. 3

ACCOUNT	DEBIT	CREDIT

NAME
SECTION
DATE

Chapter 2

Decision Case 1
(Continued)

Req. 4

Excel Application Exercise

S3-2

Req. 1

_____

_____

_____

_____

_____

_____

_____

Req. 2

_____

_____

_____

_____

_____

_____

_____

S3-4

_____

_____

_____

_____

_____

_____

Req. 1

		Journal			
DATE		ACCOUNTS AND EXPLANATIONS	POST. REF.	DEBIT	CREDIT

Req. 2

		Journal			
DATE		ACCOUNTS AND EXPLANATIONS	POST. REF.	DEBIT	CREDIT

Req. 1

		Journal			
DATE		ACCOUNTS AND EXPLANATIONS	POST. REF.	DEBIT	CREDIT

Req. 2

Req. 3

Req. 1

		Journal			
DATE		ACCOUNTS AND EXPLANATIONS	POST. REF.	DEBIT	CREDIT

Req. 2

Req. 1

		Journal			
DATE		**ACCOUNTS AND EXPLANATIONS**	**POST. REF.**	**DEBIT**	**CREDIT**

Req. 2

S3-9

		Journal			
DATE		**ACCOUNTS AND EXPLANATIONS**	**POST. REF.**	**DEBIT**	**CREDIT**

Req. 1

		Journal																				
DATE		ACCOUNTS AND EXPLANATIONS	POST. REF.				DEBIT								CREDIT							

Req. 2

Req. 1

Reqs. 1 & 2

Amount of Revenue (Expense) for July

Date	Revenue or (Expense)	Accrual Basis Amount

E3-2

E3-3

	A	B	C	D

Journal

DATE	ACCOUNTS AND EXPLANATIONS	POST. REF.	DEBIT	CREDIT

E3-6

Journal

DATE	ACCOUNTS AND EXPLANATIONS	POST. REF.	DEBIT	CREDIT

Stephen Perdue, Craftsman

Preparation of Adjusted Trial Balance

May 31, 20×8

ACCOUNT TITLE	TRIAL BALANCE		ADJUSTMENTS		ADJUSTED TRIAL BALANCE	
	DEBIT	CREDIT	DEBIT	CREDIT	DEBIT	CREDIT
Cash	3 0 0 0				3 0 0 0	
Accounts receivable	4 5 0 0				7 6 0 0	
Supplies	1 0 0 0				8 0 0	
Equipment	3 2 3 0 0				3 2 3 0 0	
Accumulated depreciation		1 4 0 0 0				1 4 4 0 0
Salary payable						9 0 0
S. Perdue, Capital		2 6 4 0 0				2 6 4 0 0
S. Perdue, withdrawals	5 1 0 0				5 1 0 0	
Service revenue		9 6 0 0				1 2 7 0 0
Salary expense	2 7 0 0				3 6 0 0	
Rent expense	1 4 0 0				1 4 0 0	
Depreciation expense					4 0 0	
Supplies expense					2 0 0	
	5 0 0 0 0	5 0 0 0 0			5 4 4 0 0	5 4 4 0 0

Journal

DATE	ACCOUNTS AND EXPLANATIONS	POST. REF.	DEBIT	CREDIT

Req. 1

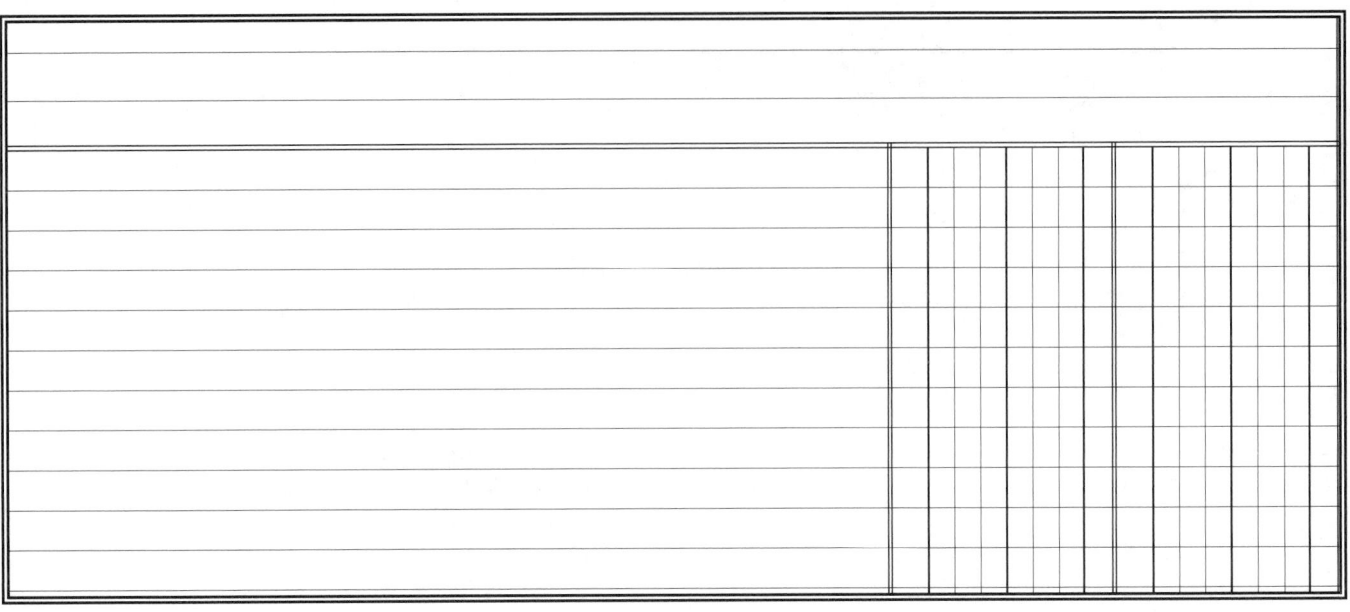

Req. 2

E3-13

Req. 1

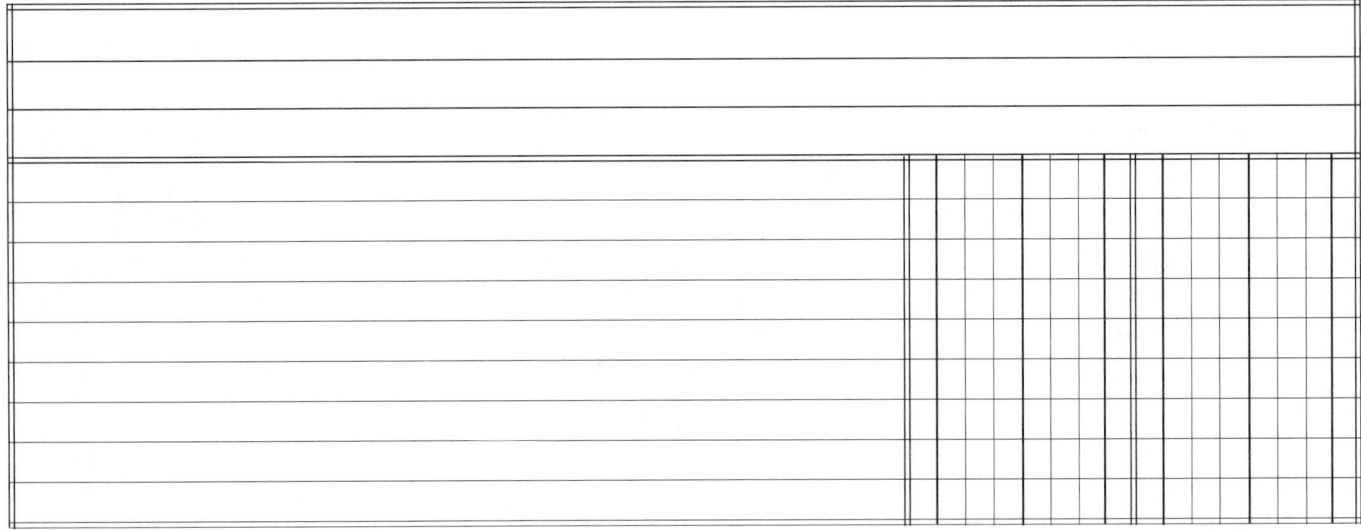

Req. 2

Reqs. 1, 3, & 6

Reqs. 1, 3, & 6 (Continued)

Req. 2

		Journal				
DATE		ACCOUNTS AND EXPLANATIONS	POST. REF.	DEBIT		CREDIT

Req. 2 (Continued)

		Journal			
DATE	ACCOUNTS AND EXPLANATIONS	POST. REF.	DEBIT	CREDIT	

Reqs. 4 & 5

ACCOUNT TITLE	TRIAL BALANCE		ADJUSTMENTS		ADJUSTED TRIAL BALANCE	
	DEBIT	CREDIT	DEBIT	CREDIT	DEBIT	CREDIT

Req. 6

		Journal			
DATE		ACCOUNTS AND EXPLANATIONS	POST. REF.	DEBIT	CREDIT

Req. 7

Req. 7 (Continued)

Req. 1

Date	Revenue (Expense)	Accrual Basis Amount

Req. 2

Req. 3

Journal

	DATE		ACCOUNTS AND EXPLANATIONS	POST. REF.	DEBIT	CREDIT
A	Dec.	31	Insurance Expense $(2,400 \cdot \frac{9}{12})$ $(2400 \cdot 9 \div 12)$		1 8 0 0	
			Prepaid Insurance			1 8 0 0
			#1 Record Insurance Expense			
B.	Dec.	31	Salary Expense $(2,000 \cdot \frac{1}{5})$		4 0 0	
			Salary Payable			4 0 0
			#3 Adjusting entry to accrued salary expense			
C.	Dec.	31	Interest Expense		6 0 0	
			Interest Payable			6 0 0
			#3			
D.	Dec.	31	Supplies Expense $(2,600 + 6,100 - 2,100)$		6 6 0 0	
			Supplies			6 6 0 0
			#1 Record supplies expense			
E.	Dec.	31	Unearned Service Revenue $(12,000 \cdot \frac{1}{4})$		3 0 0 0	
			Service Revenue			3 0 0 0
			#5 To record revenue that was collected in advance			
F.	Dec.	31	Depreciation Expense — Canoe Equipment		3 8 5 0	
			Accumulated Depreciation — Canoe Equipment			3 8 5 0
			#2			
			Depreciation Expense — Trucks		1 3 0 0	
			Accumulated Depreciation			1 3 0 0
			#2			
			Compound Entry :			
			Depreciation Expense — Canoe Equipment		3 8 5 0	
			Depreciation Expense — Trucks		1 3 0 0	
			Accumulated Depreciation — Canoe Equipment			3 8 5 0
			Accumulated Depreciation — Trucks			1 3 0 0

Journal

DATE		ACCOUNTS AND EXPLANATIONS	POST. REF.	DEBIT	CREDIT
April	30	Accounts Receivable (6,000 to 6,700) (Accounts Receivable)		700	
		Rental Revenue (9,500 to 10,200)			700
		#4 Adjusting entry to accrue rental revenue			
April	30	Interest Receivable (300-0) (Interest Receivable)		300	
		Interest Revenue (300-0)			300
		#4			
April	30	Supplies Expense (700-0) (Supplies)		700	
		Supplies (700-0)			700
		#1 (Prepaid Rent)			
April	30	Rent Expense (800-0)		800	
		Prepaid Rent (2400 to 1600)			800
		#1			
April	30	Depreciation Expense (1200-0) (Accumulated		1200	
		Accumulated Depreciation (16,000 to 17,200) Depreciation)			1200
		#2			
April	30	Wage Expense (1600 to 1900) (Wages Payable)		300	
		Wages Payable (300-0)			300
		#3			

Reqs. 1 & 2

Cash

12,200	
Balance 12,200	

Accounts Receivable

14,100	
Balance 14,100	

Prepaid Insurance

3,100	A. 2,500
Balance 600	

Supplies

800	B. 600
Balance 200	

Building

412,700	
Balance 412,700	

Accumulated Depreciation

	311,400
	900 c.
	Balance 312,500

Accounts Payable

	1,900
	D. 300
	Balance 2,200

Salary Payable

	E. 100
	Balance 100

Unearned Service Revenue

F. 1200	2,300
	Balance 1,100

Rocky Rivers, Capital

	125,000
	Balance 125,000

Rocky Rivers, Withdrawals

2,900	
Balance 2,900	

Service Revenue

	7,900
	F. 1,200
	Balance 9,100

Salary Expense

2,100	
E. 100	
Balance 2,200	

Insurance Expense

A. 2,500	
Balance 2,500	

Depreciation Expense

800	
c. 900	
Balance 900	

Advertising Expense

800	
D. 300	
Balance 1,100	

Supplies Expense

B. 600	
Balance 600	

Req. 2

DATE	ACCOUNTS AND EXPLANATIONS	POST. REF.	DEBIT	CREDIT
	Journal			
	Adjusting entries at Dec. 31, 2005			
A	Insurance Expense (3100 - 600)		2500	
	Prepaid Insurance			2500
	#1			
B	Supplies Expense (No calculation)		600	
	Supplies			600
	#1			
C	Depreciation Expense (No calculation)		900	
	Accumulated Depreciation			900
	#2			
D	Advertising Expense (No calculation)		300	
	Accounts Payable			300
	#3			
E	Salary Expense (No calculation)		100	
	Salary Payable			100
	#3			
F	Unearned Service Revenue (2300 - 1100)		1200	
	Service Revenue			1200
	#5			

Req. 3

								DEBIT						CREDIT				

Smoky Mountain Lodge
Adjusted Trial Balance Sheet
Dec. 31, 2005

ACCOUNT	DEBIT	CREDIT
Cash	1 2 2 0 0	
Accounts Receivable	1 4 1 0 0	
Prepaid Insurance	4 0 0	
Supplies	2 0 0	
Building	4 1 2 7 0 0	
Accumulated Depreciation		3 1 2 5 0 0
Accounts Payable		2 2 0 0
Salary Payable		1 0 0
Unearned Service Revenue		1 1 0 0
Rocky Rivers, Capital		1 2 5 0 0 0
Rocky Rivers, Withdrawals	2 9 0 0	
Service Revenue		9 1 0 0
Salary Expense	2 2 0 0	
Insurance Expense	2 5 0 0	
Depreciation Expense	9 0 0	
Advertising Expense	1 1 0 0	
Supplies Expense	4 0 0	
	4 5 0 0 0 0	4 5 0 0 0 0

Req. 4

Use to prepare financial statements

Req. 1

Req. 1 (Continued)

Req. 2

NAME
SECTION
DATE

D. 28,800 ÷ 4 = 7,200
7,200 ÷ 12 = 600

E. 1,000 ÷ 5 = 200

Req. 1

Pat Patillo, CPA
Prep. of Adjusted Trial Balance
July 31, 2006

ACCOUNT TITLE	TRIAL BALANCE DEBIT	TRIAL BALANCE CREDIT	ADJUSTMENTS DEBIT	ADJUSTMENTS CREDIT	ADJUSTED TRIAL BALANCE DEBIT	ADJUSTED TRIAL BALANCE CREDIT
Cash	8900				8900	
Accounts receivable	11600		(A) 900		12500	
Prepaid rent	4000			(B) 1000	3000	
Supplies	800			(C) 400	400	
Furniture	28800				28800	
Accumulated depreciation		3500		(D) 600		4100
Accounts payable		3400				3400
Salary payable				(E) 200		200
Pat Patillo, Capital		39100				39100
Pat Patillo, Withdrawals	4000				4000	
Accounting Service revenue		15000		(A) 900		15900
Salary expense	2400		(E) 200		2600	
Rent expense			(B) 1000		1000	
Utilities expense	500				500	
Depreciation expense			(D) 600		600	
Supplies expense			(C) 400		400	
	41000	41000	3100	3100	42700	67700

Req. 2

Pat Patillo, CPA				
Income Statement				
Month Ended July 31, 2006				
Revenue:				
Accounting Service Revenue				15900
Expense:				
Salary Expense		2400		
Rent Expense		1000		
Depreciation Expense		500		
Utilities Expense		600		
Supplies Expense		400		
Total Expense		5100		15900
				5100
Net Income				10800

Pat Patillo, CPA	
Statement of Owner's Equity	
Month Ended July 31, 2006	
Pat Patillo, Capital	39100
Add	
Net Income	10800
Subtract	
Withdraw	(4000)
Pat Patillo, Capital, July 31, 2006	45900

Req. 2 (Continued)

				Pat Patillo, CPA										
				Balance Sheet										
				July 31, 2006										
Assets					Liabilities									
Cash		8 9 0 0			Accounts Payable			3 4 0 0						
Accounts Receivable	1 2 5 0 0				Salary Payable			2 0 0						
Prepaid Rent		3 0 0 0			Total Liabilities			3 6 0 0						
Supplies		4 0 0												
Furniture	2 4 7 0 0				Owner's Equity									
28,800 less accumulated					Pat Patillo, Capital		4 5 9 0 0							
depreciation 4,100														
28,800 - 4100														
Total Assets		4 9 5 0 0					4 9 5 0 0							

Req. 1

Date	Revenue or (Expense)	Accrual Basis Amount

Req. 2

Req. 3

Req. 3

Unistar Alarm Systems
Adjusted Trial Balance Sheet
August 31, 2004

ACCOUNT	DEBIT	CREDIT
Cash	7 1 0 0	
Accounts Receivable	1 9 8 0 0	
Prepaid Rent	6 0 0	
Supplies	5 0 0	
Furniture	1 9 7 0 0	
Accumulated Depreciation		4 0 0 0
Accounts Payable		3 9 0 0
Salary Payable		5 0 0
Unearned Service Revenue		1 6 0 0
John Wilhelm, Capital		3 5 5 0 0
John Wilhelm, Withdrawals	5 3 0 0	
Service Revenue		1 6 8 0 0
Salary Expense	4 3 0 0	
Rent Expense	1 8 0 0	
Depreciation Expense	4 0 0	
Advertising Expense	2 1 0 0	
Supplies Expense	7 0 0	
	6 2 3 0 0	6 2 3 0 0

Req. 4

To prepare financial statements

Req. 1

Req. 1 (Continued)

Req. 2

NAME
SECTION
DATE

Chapter 3

Decision Case 1
(Continued)

Req. 3

Decision Case 2

NAME
SECTION
DATE

Chapter 3

Decision Case 2
(Continued)

Req. 1–3

NAME
SECTION
DATE

Chapter 3

Financial Statement
Case 1

Req. 1 & 3

Req. 2

		Journal			
DATE		ACCOUNTS AND EXPLANATIONS	POST. REF.	DEBIT	CREDIT

NAME
SECTION
DATE

Chapter 3

Team Project
(Continued)

NAME
SECTION
DATE

Chapter 3

Team Project

(Continued)

	Journal			
DATE	ACCOUNTS AND EXPLANATIONS	POST. REF.	DEBIT	CREDIT

Req. 1

Req. 2

Req. 3

Req. 1

		Journal			
DATE	ACCOUNTS AND EXPLANATIONS	POST. REF.	DEBIT	CREDIT

Req. 2

		Journal			
DATE		ACCOUNTS AND EXPLANATIONS	POST. REF.	DEBIT	CREDIT

Req. 3

Req. 1

		Journal			
DATE		ACCOUNTS AND EXPLANATIONS	POST. REF.	DEBIT	CREDIT

Req. 2

		Journal			
DATE		ACCOUNTS AND EXPLANATIONS	POST. REF.	DEBIT	CREDIT

Req. 3

Req. 4

DATE	ACCOUNTS AND EXPLANATIONS	POST. REF.	DEBIT	CREDIT

Req. 5

S4-2

Req. 1

		Journal			
DATE		ACCOUNTS AND EXPLANATIONS	POST. REF.	DEBIT	CREDIT

Req. 2

_____
_____
_____
_____
_____
_____
_____
_____
_____

S4-6

	Journal				
DATE	ACCOUNTS AND EXPLANATIONS	POST. REF.	DEBIT		CREDIT

S4-7

S4-10

S4-12

Day Spring Woodworking Service
Work Sheet
Month Ended September 30, 20X6

ACCOUNT TITLES	UNADJUSTED TRIAL BALANCE		ADJUSTMENTS		ADJUSTED TRIAL BALANCE		INCOME STATEMENT		BALANCE SHEET	
	DEBIT	CREDIT	DEBIT	CREDIT	DEBIT	CREDIT	DEBIT	CREDIT	DEBIT	CREDIT
Cash	3 5 0 0									
Accounts receivable	3 4 0 0									
Prepaid rent	1 2 0 0									
Supplies	3 3 0 0									
Equipment	3 2 6 0 0									
Accumulated depreciation		1 8 0 0								
Accounts payable		3 6 0 0								
Salary payable										
Gail Pfeiffer, Capital		3 6 0 0 0								
Gail Pfeiffer, Withdrawals	2 0 0 0									
Service revenue		7 1 0 0								
Depreciation expense										
Salary expense	1 8 0 0									
Rent expense										
Utilities expense	7 0 0									
Supplies expense										
	4 8 5 0 0	4 8 5 0 0								
Net income										

Journal

DATE	ACCOUNTS AND EXPLANATIONS	POST. REF.	DEBIT	CREDIT

ACCOUNT	DEBIT	CREDIT

Req. 1

Req. 2

Journal

DATE	ACCOUNTS AND EXPLANATIONS	POST. REF.	DEBIT	CREDIT

Req. 2 (Continued)

E4-6

			Journal	POST. REF.		DEBIT			CREDIT	
DATE		ACCOUNTS AND EXPLANATIONS								

Journal

DATE	ACCOUNTS AND EXPLANATIONS	POST. REF.	DEBIT	CREDIT

Req. 1

		Journal				
DATE	ACCOUNTS AND EXPLANATIONS	POST. REF.	DEBIT		CREDIT	

Req. 2

Req. 1

Journal				
DATE	ACCOUNTS AND EXPLANATIONS	POST. REF.	DEBIT	CREDIT

Req. 2

Req. 1

Req. 2

Req. 1

	Journal			
		POST.		
DATE	ACCOUNTS AND EXPLANATIONS	REF.	DEBIT	CREDIT

Req. 1 (continued)

Req. 2

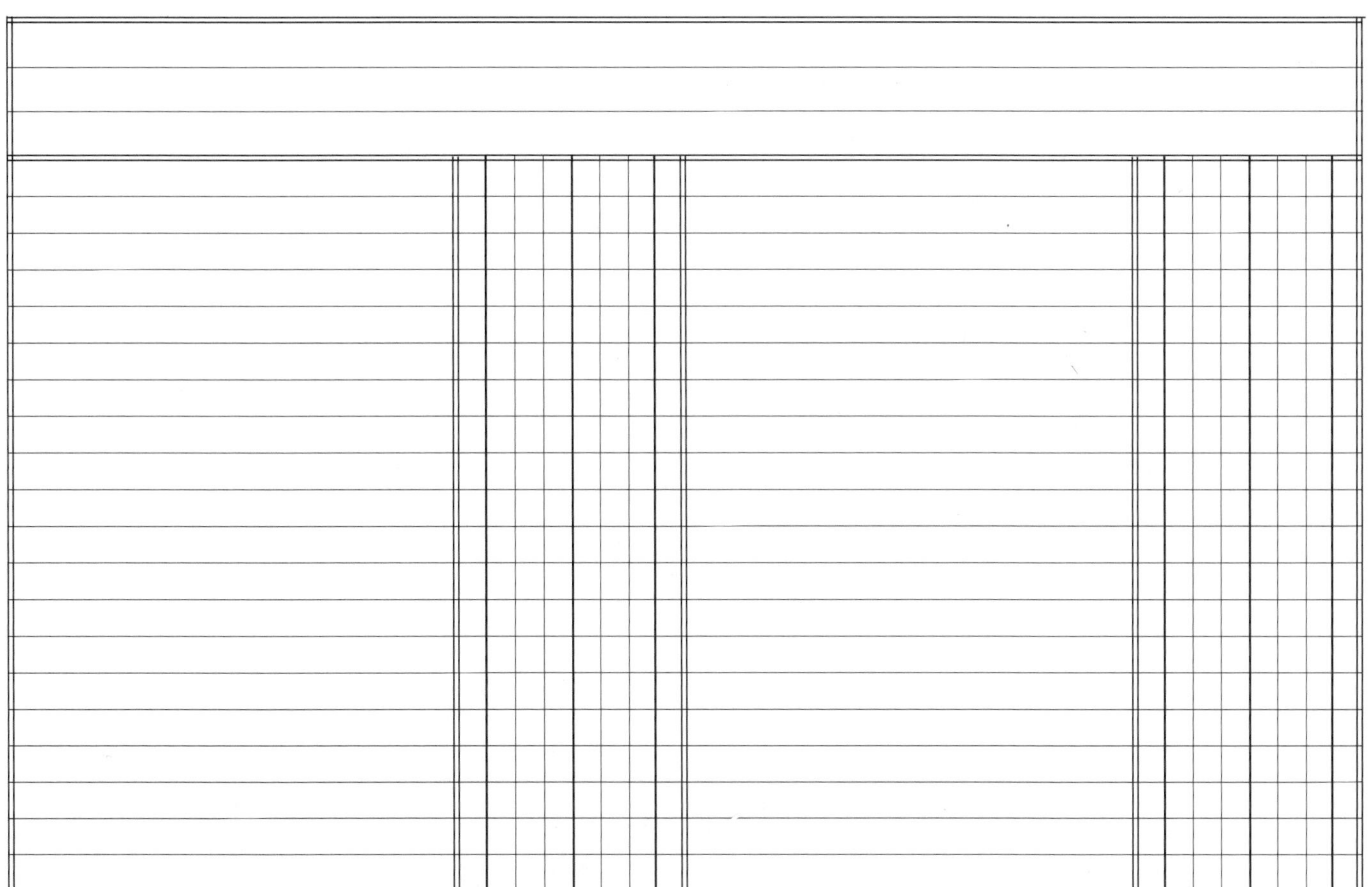

Req. 3

Marsha walker, Consultant
Accounting Work Sheet
December 31, 20XX

ACCOUNT TITLES	UNADJUSTED TRIAL BALANCE		ADJUSTMENTS		ADJUSTED TRIAL BALANCE		INCOME STATEMENT		BALANCE SHEET	
	DEBIT	CREDIT	DEBIT	CREDIT	DEBIT	CREDIT	DEBIT	CREDIT	DEBIT	CREDIT
Cash	11700				11700					
Accounts receivable	1100		(a) 400		1500					
Supplies	300			(c) 200	100					
Equipment	2000				2000					
Accumulated depr. equip.				(d1) 50		50				
Furniture	3600				3600					
Accumulated depr.-furn.				(d2) 60		60				
Accounts payable		3600				3600				
Salary payable				(e) 500		500				
Unearned service revenue		900	(b) 300			600				
Marsha Walker, Capital		14000				14000				
Marsha Walker, Withdrawals	1600				1600					
Service revenue		2500		(a) 400		3200				
				(b) 300						
Rent expense	500				500					
Utilities expense	200				200					
Salary expense			(e) 500		500					
Depreciation expense-equip			(d1) 50		50					
Depreciation expense-furn.			(d2) 60		60					
Supplies expense			(c) 200		200					
	21000	21000	1510	1510	22010	22010				
Net income										

Lane's Interiors
Work Sheet
Month Ended May 31, 20X8

Account Titles	Unadjusted Trial Balance Debit	Unadjusted Trial Balance Credit	Adjustments Debit	Adjustments Credit	Adjusted Trial Balance Debit	Adjusted Trial Balance Credit	Income Statement Debit	Income Statement Credit	Balance Sheet Debit	Balance Sheet Credit
Cash	4300				4300				4300	
Notes receivable	10300				10300				10300	
Interest receivable			(H) 200		200				200	
Supplies	500			(C) 100	400				400	
Prepaid insurance	1700			(D) 300	1400				1400	
Furniture	27400				27400				27400	
Accum. depr.–furniture		1400		(A) 500		1900				1900
Building	53900				53900				53900	
Accum. depr.–building		34500		(A) 400		34900				34900
Land	18700				18700				18700	
Accounts payable		14700		(G) 100		14800				14800
Interest payable				(E) 200		200				200
Salary payable				(B) 600		600				600
Unearned service revenue		8800	(F) 4400			4400				4400
Notes payable, long-term		18700				18700				18700
K.Lane, Capital		29900				29900				29900
K.Lane, Withdrawals	3800				3800				3800	
Service revenue		16800		(F) 4400		21200		21200		
Interest revenue				(H) 200		200		200		
Depr. expense–furniture			(A) 500		500		500			
Depr. expense–building			(A) 400		400		400			
Salary expense	2100		(B) 600		2700		2700			
Insurance expense			(D) 300		300		300			
Interest expense			(E) 200		200		200			
Utilities expense	1100				1100		1100			
Advertising expense	1000		(G) 100		1100		1100			
Supplies expense			(C) 100		100		100			
	124800	124800	6800	6800	126800	126800	6400	21400	120400	105400
Net income							15000			15000
							21400	21400	120400	120400

C. 500 – 400 = 100

227

P4-2A

Req. 1

Ross Reagan, M.D.
Work Sheet
Year Ended December 31, 20X5

ACCOUNT TITLES	UNADJUSTED TRIAL BALANCE		ADJUSTMENTS		ADJUSTED TRIAL BALANCE		INCOME STATEMENT		BALANCE SHEET	
	DEBIT	CREDIT	DEBIT	CREDIT	DEBIT	CREDIT	DEBIT	CREDIT	DEBIT	CREDIT
Cash	29000									
Accounts receivable	44000									
Supplies	6000									
Equipment	102000									
Accumulated depr.		12000								
Accounts payable		16000								
Salary payable										
Unearned service reven.		2000								
Note payable, long-term		40000								
Ross Reagan, Capital		41000								
Ross Reagan, Withdrawals	54000									
Service revenue		175000								
Salary expense	36000									
Supplies expense										
Depreciation expense										
Interest expense	5000									
Insurance expense	10000									
	286000	286000								
Net income										

Req. 2

Req. 3

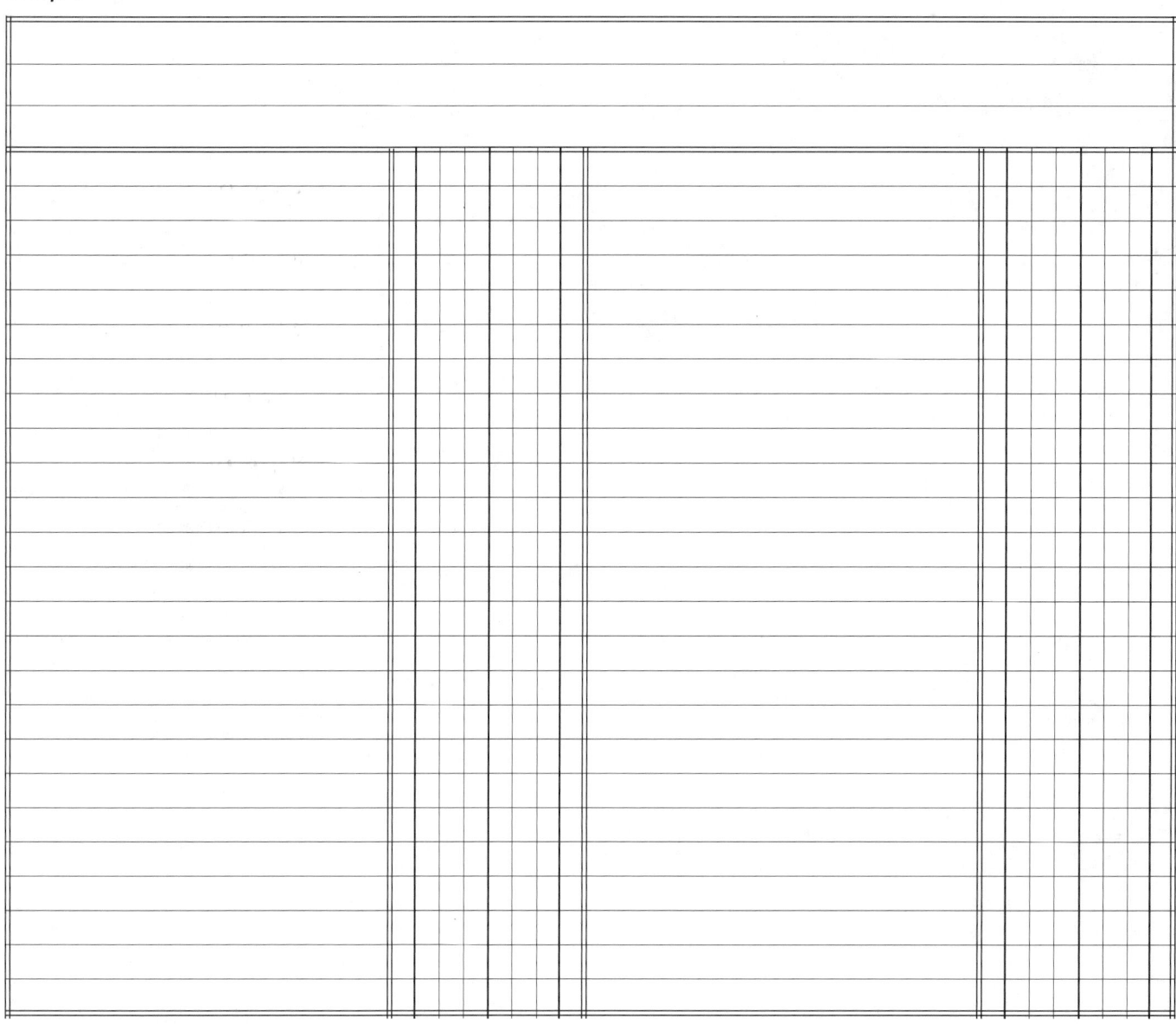

Req. 4

Req. 1

	Journal						
		POST. REF.	**DEBIT**			**CREDIT**	
DATE	**ACCOUNTS AND EXPLANATIONS**						
	Adjusting Entries						
A	Accounts Receivable		2 2 0 0				
	Service Revenue					2 2 0 0	
B	Depreciation Expense on Equipment		6 9 0 0				
	Accumulated Depreciation - Equipment					6 9 0 0	
	Depreciation Expense - Building		3 7 0 0				
	Accumulated Depreciation - Building					3 7 0 0	
C	Wage Expense		8 0 0				
	Wages Payable					8 0 0	
D	Unearned Service Revenue		4 1 0 0				
	Service Revenue					4 1 0 0	
E	Supplies Expense		5 0 0				
	Supplies					5 0 0	
F	Insurance Expense		7 0 0				
	Prepaid Insurance					7 0 0	
G	Interest Expense		1 2 0 0				
	Interest Payable					1 2 0 0	

Req. 2

		Journal				
DATE		**ACCOUNTS AND EXPLANATIONS**	**POST. REF.**	**DEBIT**	**CREDIT**	
April	30	Service Revenue (98,500 + 2,200 + 4,100 = 104,800)		104800		
	30	Income Summary			104800	
April	30	Income Summary (All expenses added up)		71500		
		Depreciation Expense - Equipment			6900	
		Depreciation Expense - Building			3700	
		Wage Expense (32,800 + 800 = 33,600)			33600	
		Insurance Expense (5,100 + 700 = 5,800)			5800	
		Interest Expense (8,100 + 1,200 = 9,300)			9300	
		Utilities Expense			4900	
		Supplies Expense (6,800 + 500 = 7,300)			7300	
April	30	Income Summary (104,800 - 71,500)		33300		
	30	Jeff Trichel, Capital			33300	
April	30	Jeff Trichel, Capital		27500		
		Jeff Trichel, Withdrawals			27500	

Reqs. 1 & 4

ACCOUNT	Cash					ACCOUNT NO.		
						BALANCE		
DATE	ITEM	JRNL. REF.	DEBIT	CREDIT		DEBIT		CREDIT

ACCOUNT						ACCOUNT NO.		
						BALANCE		
DATE	ITEM	JRNL. REF.	DEBIT	CREDIT		DEBIT		CREDIT

ACCOUNT						ACCOUNT NO.		
						BALANCE		
DATE	ITEM	JRNL. REF.	DEBIT	CREDIT		DEBIT		CREDIT

ACCOUNT						ACCOUNT NO.		
						BALANCE		
DATE	ITEM	JRNL. REF.	DEBIT	CREDIT		DEBIT		CREDIT

Reqs. 1 & 4 (Continued)

ACCOUNT						ACCOUNT NO.	
						BALANCE	
DATE	ITEM	JRNL. REF.	DEBIT	CREDIT		DEBIT	CREDIT

ACCOUNT						ACCOUNT NO.	
						BALANCE	
DATE	ITEM	JRNL. REF.	DEBIT	CREDIT		DEBIT	CREDIT

ACCOUNT						ACCOUNT NO.	
						BALANCE	
DATE	ITEM	JRNL. REF.	DEBIT	CREDIT		DEBIT	CREDIT

ACCOUNT						ACCOUNT NO.	
						BALANCE	
DATE	ITEM	JRNL. REF.	DEBIT	CREDIT		DEBIT	CREDIT

Reqs. 1 & 4 (Continued)

ACCOUNT						ACCOUNT NO.		
						BALANCE		
DATE	ITEM	JRNL. REF.	DEBIT		CREDIT		DEBIT	CREDIT

ACCOUNT						ACCOUNT NO.		
						BALANCE		
DATE	ITEM	JRNL. REF.	DEBIT		CREDIT		DEBIT	CREDIT

ACCOUNT						ACCOUNT NO.		
						BALANCE		
DATE	ITEM	JRNL. REF.	DEBIT		CREDIT		DEBIT	CREDIT

ACCOUNT						ACCOUNT NO.		
						BALANCE		
DATE	ITEM	JRNL. REF.	DEBIT		CREDIT		DEBIT	CREDIT

Reqs. 1 & 4 (Continued)

ACCOUNT					ACCOUNT NO.	
					BALANCE	
DATE	ITEM	JRNL. REF.	DEBIT	CREDIT	DEBIT	CREDIT

ACCOUNT					ACCOUNT NO.	
					BALANCE	
DATE	ITEM	JRNL. REF.	DEBIT	CREDIT	DEBIT	CREDIT

ACCOUNT					ACCOUNT NO.	
					BALANCE	
DATE	ITEM	JRNL. REF.	DEBIT	CREDIT	DEBIT	CREDIT

ACCOUNT					ACCOUNT NO.	
					BALANCE	
DATE	ITEM	JRNL. REF.	DEBIT	CREDIT	DEBIT	CREDIT

Reqs. 1 & 4 (Continued)

ACCOUNT							ACCOUNT NO.			
								BALANCE		
DATE	ITEM	JRNL. REF.	DEBIT		CREDIT		DEBIT		CREDIT	

ACCOUNT							ACCOUNT NO.			
								BALANCE		
DATE	ITEM	JRNL. REF.	DEBIT		CREDIT		DEBIT		CREDIT	

NAME
SECTION
DATE

Req. 2

Lange Party Productions
Work Sheet
Month Ended October 31, 20X6

ACCOUNT TITLES	UNADJUSTED TRIAL BALANCE DEBIT	UNADJUSTED TRIAL BALANCE CREDIT	ADJUSTMENTS DEBIT	ADJUSTMENTS CREDIT	ADJUSTED TRIAL BALANCE DEBIT	ADJUSTED TRIAL BALANCE CREDIT	INCOME STATEMENT DEBIT	INCOME STATEMENT CREDIT	BALANCE SHEET DEBIT	BALANCE SHEET CREDIT
Cash	4900				4900				4900	
Accounts receivable	15310				15310				15310	
Prepaid rent	2200			B 200	2000				2000	
Supplies	840			C 770	70				70	
Equipment	26830				26830				26830	
Accum. depr.—equip.		3400		D 250		3650				3650
Accounts payable		7290				7290				7290
Salary payable				E 310		310				310
Unearned service revenue		5300	A 4500			800				800
Melanie Lange, Capital		28290				28290				28290
Melanie Lange, Withdrawals	3900				3900				3900	
Service revenue		12560		A 4500		17060		17060		
Salary expense	2860		E 310		3170		3170			
Rent expense			B 200		200		200			
Depreciation exp.—equip.			D 250		250		250			
Supplies expense			C 770		770		770			
	56840	56840	6030	6030	57400	57400	4390	17060	53010	40340
Net income							12670			12670
							17060	17060	53010	53010

40340 + 12670 = 53010

17060 - Expenses = 12670
(4390)

A. 5,300 - 800 = 4,500

B. 2,200 - 2,000 = 200

Req. 3

Req. 3 (Continued)

Book pg. 149

Req. 4

		Journal						
DATE		ACCOUNTS AND EXPLANATIONS	POST. REF.	DEBIT		CREDIT	
Oct.	31	Service Revenue		1 7 0 6 0			
		Income Summary				1 7 0 6 0
Oct.	31	Income Summary		4 3 9 0			
		Salary Expense (2,860 + 310 = 3170)				3 1 7 0
		Rent Expense				2 0 0
		Depreciation Expense - Equipment				2 5 0
		Supplies Expense				7 7 0
Oct.	31	Income Summary (17060 - 4390 = 12670)		1 2 6 7 0			
		Melanie Lange, Capital				1 2 6 7 0
Oct.	31	Melanie Lange, Capital		3 9 0 0			
		Melanie Lange, Withdrawal				3 9 0 0

Req. 5

	Lange Party Productions									
	Postclosing Trial Balance									
	October 31, 2006									
Cash			4	9	0	0				
Accounts Receivable		1	5	3	1	0				
Prepaid Rent			2	0	0	0				
Supplies					7	0				
Equipment		2	6	8	3	0				
Accumulated Depreciation — Equipment							3	6	5	0
Accounts Payable							7	2	9	0
Salary Payable								3	1	0
Unearned Service Revenue								8	0	0
Melanie Lange, Capital							3	7	0	6	0
		4	9	1	1	0	4	9	1	1	0

Capital = 28290 + 12670 = 40960 - 3900 = 37060

Req. 1

Req. 2

Req. a

Req. b

				Journal																			

DATE	ACCOUNTS AND EXPLANATIONS	POST. REF.	DEBIT	CREDIT

Reqs. c & d

NAME
SECTION
DATE

Roadster Tune Center
Work Sheet
Month Ended June 30, 20X3

ACCOUNT TITLES	UNADJUSTED TRIAL BALANCE		ADJUSTMENTS		ADJUSTED TRIAL BALANCE		INCOME STATEMENT		BALANCE SHEET	
	DEBIT	CREDIT	DEBIT	CREDIT	DEBIT	CREDIT	DEBIT	CREDIT	DEBIT	CREDIT
Cash	2 1 2 0 0									
Accounts receivable	3 7 8 0 0									
Supplies	1 7 6 0 0									
Prepaid insurance	2 3 0 0									
Equipment	3 2 6 0 0									
Accumulated depr.–equip.		2 6 2 0 0								
Building	4 2 8 0 0									
Accumulated depr.–bldg.		1 0 5 0 0								
Land	2 8 3 0 0									
Accounts payable		2 2 6 0 0								
Interest payable										
Wages payable										
Unearned service revenue		1 0 5 0 0								
Note payable, long-term		2 2 4 0 0								
Dan Runyan, Capital		7 9 1 0 0								
Dan Runyan, Withdrawals	4 2 0 0									
Service revenue		2 0 1 0 0								
Depr. expense–equip										
Depr. expense–bldg.										
Wage expense	3 2 0 0									
Insurance expense										
Interest expense										
Utilities expense	1 1 0 0									
Advertising expense	3 0 0									
Supplies expense										
Net income	1 9 1 4 0 0	1 9 1 4 0 0								

Req. 1

Lake Air Studio
Work Sheet
Year Ended December 31, 20X6

ACCOUNT TITLES	UNADJUSTED TRIAL BALANCE		ADJUSTMENTS		ADJUSTED TRIAL BALANCE		INCOME STATEMENT		BALANCE SHEET	
	DEBIT	CREDIT	DEBIT	CREDIT	DEBIT	CREDIT	DEBIT	CREDIT	DEBIT	CREDIT
Cash	15000									
Accounts receivable	36000									
Supplies	9000									
Equipment	99000									
Accumulated depreciation		13000								
Accounts payable		6000								
Salary payable										
Unearned service revenue		5000								
Note payable, long-term		60000								
Besty Willis, Capital		36000								
Besty Willis, Withdrawals	62000									
Service revenue		182000								
Salary expense	53000									
Supplies expense										
Depreciation expense										
Interest expense	6000									
Rent expense	15000									
Insurance expense	7000									
	302000	302000								
Net income										

Req. 2

Req. 2 (Continued)

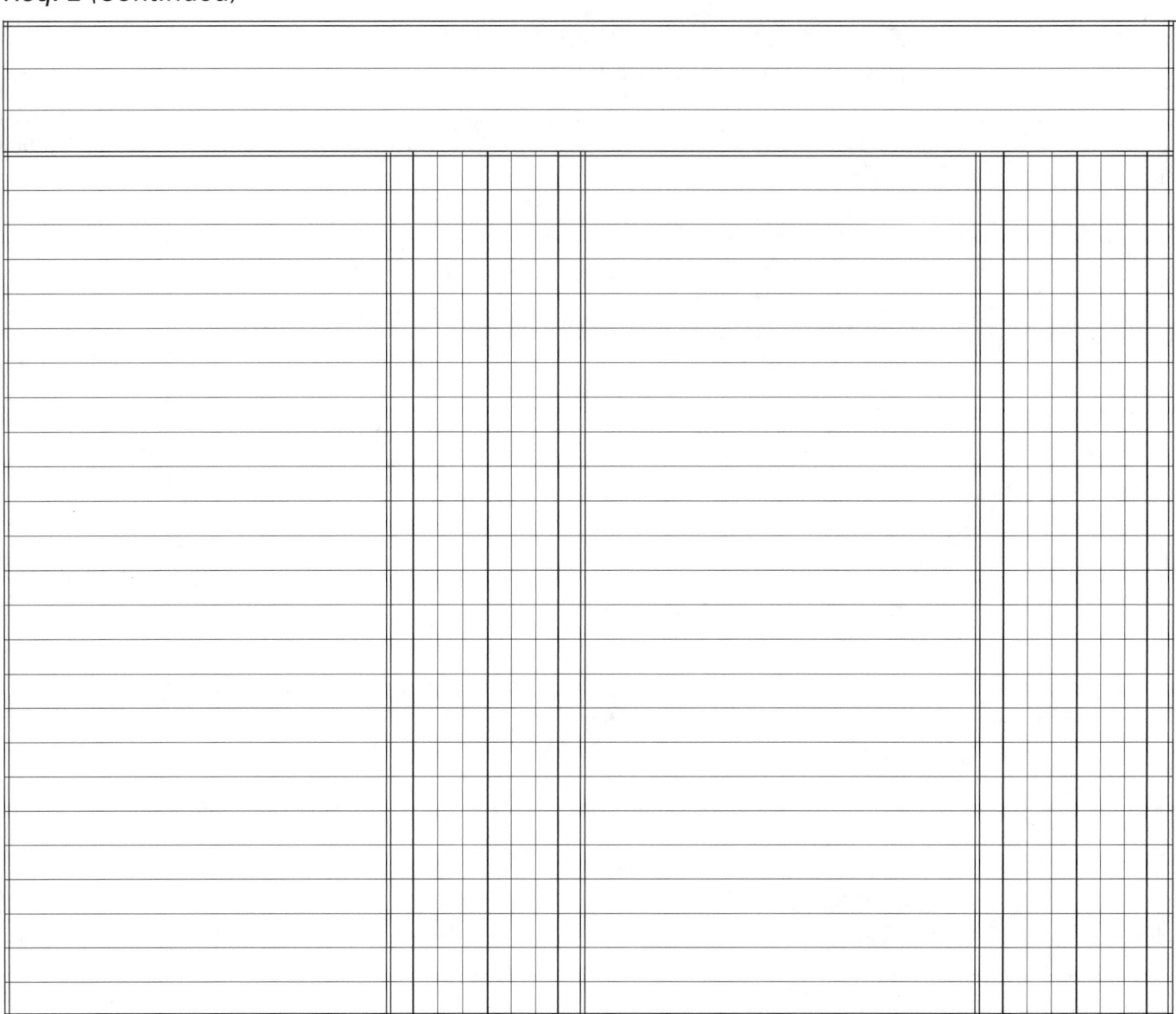

Req. 3

Req. 1

Req. 2

Req. a

Req. b

Journal

DATE	ACCOUNTS AND EXPLANATIONS	POST. REF.	DEBIT	CREDIT

Reqs. c & d

Reqs. 1–3

NAME
SECTION
DATE

Chapter 4

**Financial
Statement Case**

Reqs. 1 – 5

Team Project

Req. 1

NAME
SECTION
DATE

Chapter 4

Team Project
(Continued)

Req. 2

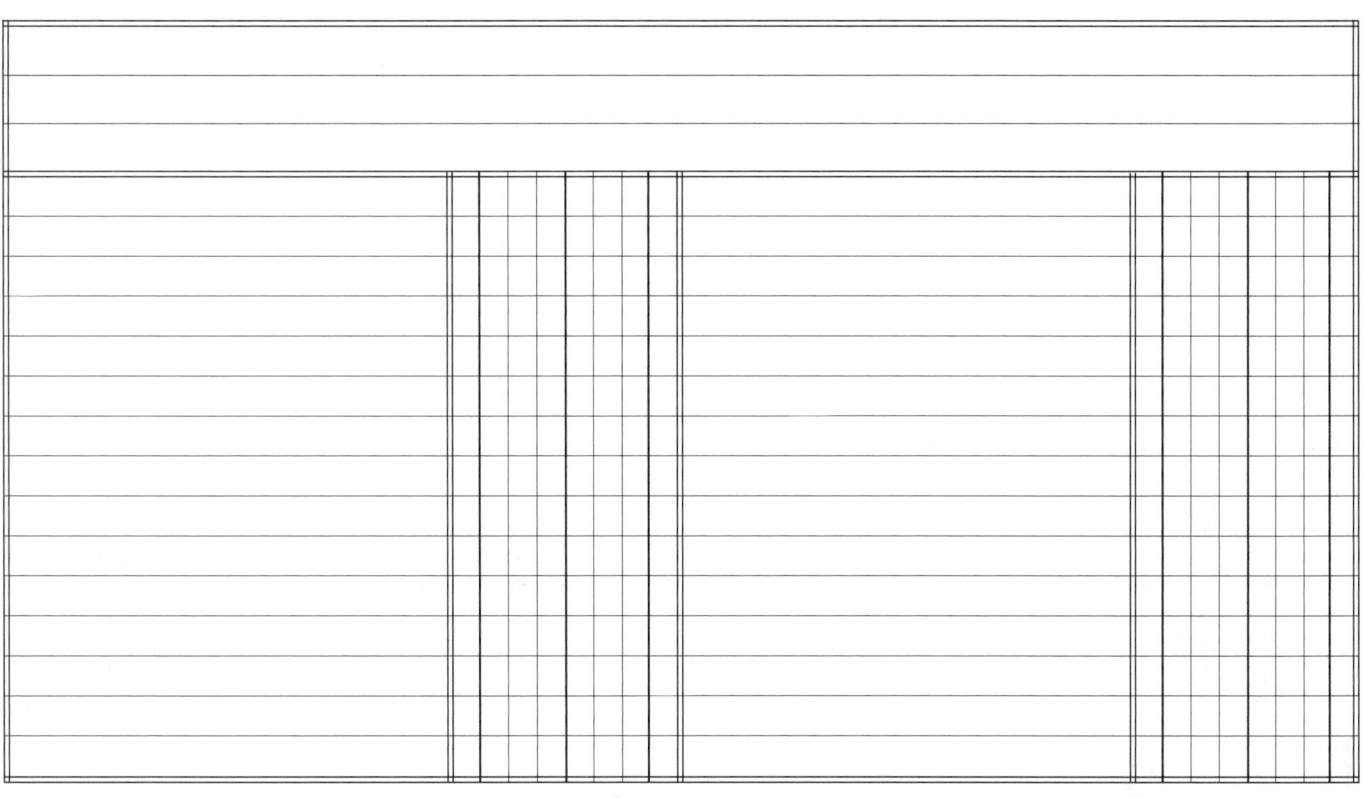

Req. 3

_____

_____

_____

_____

Reqs. 1, 2, & 3

Reqs. 2 & 3

		Journal			
DATE		ACCOUNTS AND EXPLANATIONS	POST. REF.	DEBIT	CREDIT

Req. 4

	Journal				
DATE	**ACCOUNTS AND EXPLANATIONS**	**POST. REF.**	**DEBIT**	**CREDIT**	

		Journal				
DATE		ACCOUNTS AND EXPLANATIONS	POST. REQ.	DEBIT		CREDIT

S5-2

Journal

DATE	ACCOUNTS AND EXPLANATIONS	POST. REQ.	DEBIT	CREDIT

S5-4

Journal

DATE	ACCOUNTS AND EXPLANATIONS	POST. REQ.	DEBIT	CREDIT

		Journal			
DATE		ACCOUNTS AND EXPLANATIONS	POST. REQ.	DEBIT	CREDIT

Journal

DATE	ACCOUNTS AND EXPLANATIONS	POST. REQ.	DEBIT	CREDIT

S5-8

Journal

DATE	ACCOUNTS AND EXPLANATIONS	POST. REQ.	DEBIT	CREDIT

Journal

DATE	ACCOUNTS AND EXPLANATIONS	POST. REQ.	DEBIT	CREDIT

S5-11

Reqs. 1, 2 and 3

Journal

DATE	ACCOUNTS AND EXPLANATIONS	POST. REQ.	DEBIT	CREDIT

E5-2

Journal

DATE	ACCOUNTS AND EXPLANATIONS	POST. REQ.	DEBIT	CREDIT

Journal

DATE	ACCOUNTS AND EXPLANATIONS	POST. REQ.	DEBIT	CREDIT

Journal

DATE	ACCOUNTS AND EXPLANATIONS	POST. REQ.	DEBIT	CREDIT

		2001		2000	

Sales	Sales Discounts	Net Sales	Cost of Goods Sold	Gross Profit

Computations

a. _____

b. _____

c. _____

d. _____

e. _____

f. _____

g. _____

h. _____

Req.1

		Journal				
DATE		ACCOUNTS AND EXPLANATIONS	POST. REQ.	DEBIT		CREDIT

Req. 2

Req.1

			Journal				
DATE		ACCOUNTS AND EXPLANATIONS		POST. REQ.	DEBIT	CREDIT	

Req. 1

Req. 2

Dollar amounts in millions

20 × 4

Reqs. 1 & 2

Req. 2

		Journal			
DATE	ACCOUNTS AND EXPLANATIONS	POST. REQ.	DEBIT	CREDIT	

Req. 2 (Continued)

Journal

DATE	ACCOUNTS AND EXPLANATIONS	POST. REQ.	DEBIT	CREDIT

After Closing

Total Debits in the ledger

Total Credits in the ledger

Req. 3

NAME
SECTION
DATE

Chapter 5

pg. 220

P5-2A

Journal

Walgreen's Entries

DATE		ACCOUNTS AND EXPLANATIONS	POST. REQ.	DEBIT	CREDIT
June	8	Inventory (4,000 + 200 = 6200)		6 2 0 0	
		Accounts Payable			6 2 0 0
June	11	Accounts Payable		1 0 0 0	
		Inventory			1 0 0 0
June	17	Accounts Payable		2 0 0 0	
		Inventory (2,000 x 0.02 = 40 then 2,000 - 40 = 1960)			4 0
		Cash			1 9 6 0
June	26	Accounts Payable (6,200 - 1,000 = 5,200 - 2,000 = 3,200)		3 2 0 0	
		Cash			3 2 0 0
		Procter & Gamble's Entries			
June	8	Accounts Receivable		4 0 0 0	
		Sales Revenue			4 0 0 0
		Cost of Goods Sold		2 1 0 0	
		Inventory			2 1 0 0
		Accounts Receivable		2 0 0	
		Cash			2 0 0
June	11	Sales Returns and Allowances		1 0 0 0	
		Accounts Receivable			1 0 0 0
		Inventory		4 0 0	
		Cost of Goods Sold			4 0 0
June	17	Cash		1 9 6 0	
		Sales Discounts		4 0	
		Accounts Receivable			2 0 0 0
June	26	Cash (4,000 + 200 - 1,000 - 2,000 = 3,200)		3 2 0 0	
		Accounts Receivable			3 2 0 0

pg. 191
pg. 192

		Journal				
DATE		ACCOUNTS AND EXPLANATIONS	POST. REQ.	DEBIT		CREDIT

Req. 1

		Journal				
DATE		**ACCOUNTS AND EXPLANATIONS**	**POST. REQ.**	**DEBIT**	**CREDIT**	
July	2	Inventory		800		
		Cash			800	
July	5	Supplies		600		
		Accounts Payable			600	
July	8	Inventory (3,000 + 230 = 3230)		3230		
		Accounts Payable			3230	
July	9	Cash		1200		
		Sales Revenue			1200	
		Cost of Goods Sold		700		
		Inventory			700	
July	11	Accounts Payable		200		
		Inventory			200	
July	12	Inventory		3330		
		Accounts Payable			3330	
July	14	Accounts Receivable		9600		
		Sales Revenue			9600	
		Cost of Goods Sold		5000		
		Inventory			5000	
July	16	Utilities Expense		275		
		Cash			275	
July	20	Sales Returns and Allowances		400		
		Accounts Receivable			400	
		Inventory		250		
		Cost of Goods Sold			250	
July	21	Cash		2946		
		Note Payable			2946	

pg, 192

Req. 1 (Continued)

Journal

DATE		ACCOUNTS AND EXPLANATIONS	POST. REQ.	DEBIT	CREDIT
July	21	Accounts Payable (3,230 - 230 = 3,000 - 200 = 2800)		3030	
		Inventory (3,230 - 200 = 3,030) (2,800×0.03)			84
		Cash (3,230 - 230 = 3,000 - 200 = 2800 × 0.03 = 84)			2946
July	23	Cash (7,000 × 0.02 = 140)		6860	
		Sales Discounts		140	
		Accounts Receivable			7000
July	30	Accounts Payable		400	
		Cash			400

Req. 2

July 20   July 23
↓   ↓

9,600 - 400 = 9,200 - 7,000 = 2,200 - July 31

No cash discount

Req. 1

pg. 204

Academy Security Systems									
Income Statement									
Year Ended June 30, 2008									
Sales Revenue					1 9 9 1 0 0				
Less: Sales Discounts		(3 4 0 0)							
Sales Returns and Allowances		(1 2 1 0 0)		(1 5 5 0 0)					
Net Sales Revenue							1 8 3 6 0 0		
Cost of Goods Sold							(9 5 0 0 0)		
Gross Profit							8 8 6 0 0		
Operating Expenses:									
Selling Expenses					1 9 8 0 0				
General Expenses					1 6 3 0 0		3 6 1 0 0		
Net Income (88,600 - 36,100 = 52,500)							5 2 5 0 0		

Req. 2

No, he did not.

NAME
SECTION
DATE

ACCOUNT TITLE	TRIAL BALANCE		ADJUSTMENTS		INCOME STATEMENT		BALANCE SHEET	
	DEBIT	CREDIT	DEBIT	CREDIT	DEBIT	CREDIT	DEBIT	CREDIT
Cash								
Accounts receivable								
Inventory								
Store supplies								
Prepaid insurance								
Store fixtures								
Accumulated depreciation								
Accounts payable								
Salary Payable								
Interest payable								
Note payable, long-term								
Elaine Lorens, capital								
Elaine Lorens, withdrawals								
Sales revenue								
Cost of goods sold								
Salary expense								
Rent expense								
Utilities expense								
Depreciation expense								
Insurance expense								
Store supplies expense								
Interest expense								
Net Income								

Req.1

Journal

	DATE		ACCOUNTS AND EXPLANATIONS	POST. REQ.	DEBIT	CREDIT
A.	Dec.	31	Insurance Expense (6090 - 5300)		7 9 0	7 9 0
			Prepaid Insurance			
B.	Dec.	31	Depreciation Expense (63,900 ÷ 10)		6 3 9 0	6 3 9 0
			Accumulated Depreciation			
C.	Dec.	31	Salary Expense		1 2 6 0	1 2 6 0
			Salary Payable			
D.	Dec.	31	Interest Expense		8 7 0	8 7 0
			Interest Payable			
E.	Dec.	31	Supplies Expense (1,990 - 760)		1 2 3 0	1 2 3 0
			Supplies			
F.	Dec.	31	Cost of Goods Sold (101,760 - 94,780)		6 9 8 0	6 9 8 0
			Inventory			

Req.1 (Continued)

<table>
<tr><td colspan="6" align="center">**Journal**</td></tr>
<tr><td colspan="6">Closing Entries</td></tr>
<tr><td>DATE</td><td>ACCOUNTS AND EXPLANATIONS</td><td>POST. REQ.</td><td>DEBIT</td><td></td><td>CREDIT</td></tr>
<tr><td></td><td>Sales Revenue</td><td></td><td>290000</td><td></td><td></td></tr>
<tr><td></td><td>   Income Summary</td><td></td><td></td><td></td><td>290000</td></tr>
<tr><td></td><td>Income Summary</td><td></td><td>255000</td><td></td><td></td></tr>
<tr><td></td><td>   Cost of Goods Sold (161,090 + 6980 =168,070)</td><td></td><td></td><td></td><td>168070</td></tr>
<tr><td></td><td>   Salary Expense   (46,580 + 1260 = 47840)</td><td></td><td></td><td></td><td>47840</td></tr>
<tr><td></td><td>   Rent Expense</td><td></td><td></td><td></td><td>14630</td></tr>
<tr><td></td><td>   Utilities Expense</td><td></td><td></td><td></td><td>6780</td></tr>
<tr><td></td><td>   Depreciation Expense</td><td></td><td></td><td></td><td>6390</td></tr>
<tr><td></td><td>   Insurance Expense   (5300 + 790 =</td><td></td><td></td><td></td><td>6090</td></tr>
<tr><td></td><td>   Store Supplies Expense</td><td></td><td></td><td></td><td>1230</td></tr>
<tr><td></td><td>   Interest Expense (3100 + 870 =</td><td></td><td></td><td></td><td>3970</td></tr>
<tr><td></td><td>Income Summary   (290,000 - 255,000 =35,000)</td><td></td><td>35000</td><td></td><td></td></tr>
<tr><td></td><td>   Elaine Lorens, Capital</td><td></td><td></td><td></td><td>35000</td></tr>
<tr><td></td><td>Elaine Lorens, Capital</td><td></td><td>36300</td><td></td><td></td></tr>
<tr><td></td><td>   Elaine Lorens, Withdrawals</td><td></td><td></td><td></td><td>36300</td></tr>
</table>

Req.2

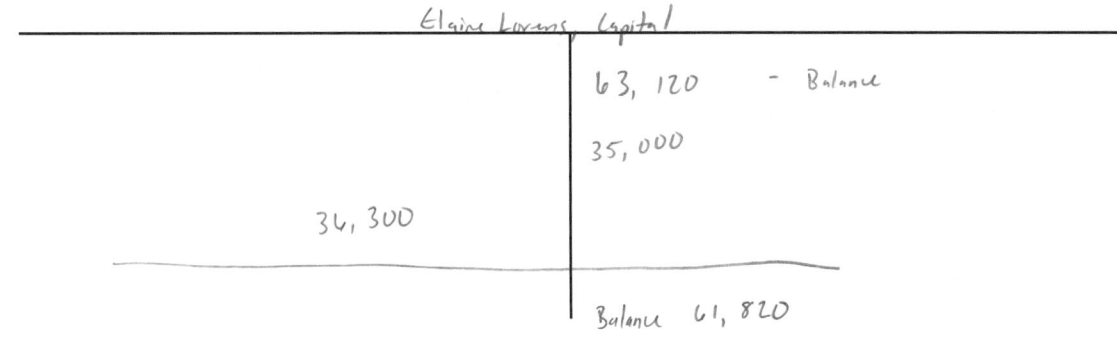

Elaine Lorens, Capital

	63, 120 - Balance
	35,000
36, 300	
	Balance 61, 820

Req. 1

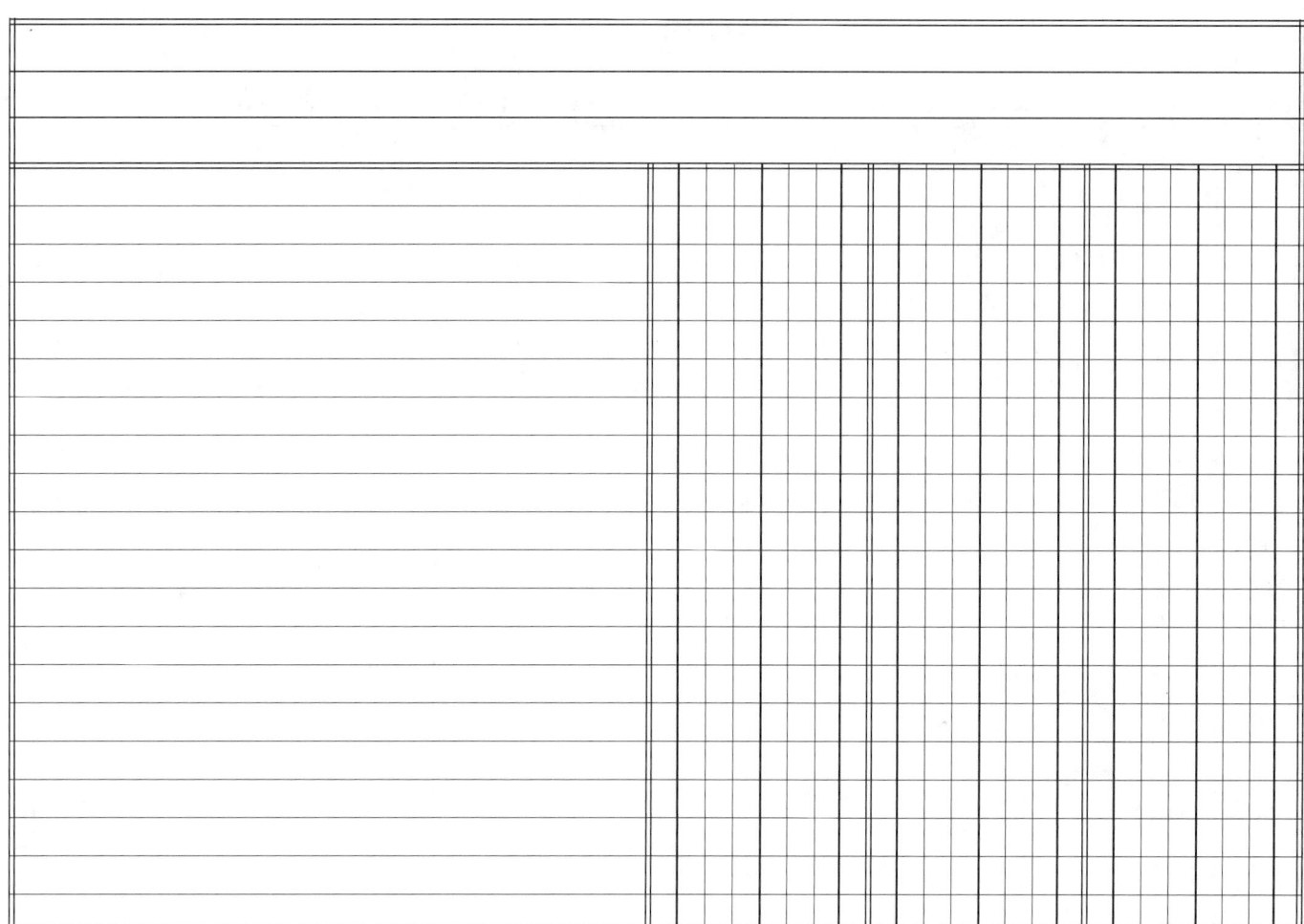

Req. 2

Req. 1

Req. 2

Req. 1

Req. 2

NAME
SECTION
DATE

ACCOUNT TITLE	TRIAL BALANCE		ADJUSTMENTS		INCOME STATEMENT		BALANCE SHEET	
	DEBIT	CREDIT	DEBIT	CREDIT	DEBIT	CREDIT	DEBIT	CREDIT
Cash								
Accounts receivable								
Inventory								
Prepaid rent								
Fixtures								
Accumulated depreciation								
Accounts payable								
Salary payable								
Interest payable								
Note payable, long-term								
Jacob Xiang, capital								
Jacob Xiang, withdrawals								
Sales revenue								
Cost of goods sold								
Salary expense								
Rent expense								
Advertising expense								
Utilities expense								
Depreciation expense								
Insurance expense								
Interest expense								
Net Income								

Req.1

		Journal				
DATE		ACCOUNTS AND EXPLANATIONS	POST. REQ.	DEBIT		CREDIT
		.				

Req.1 (Continued)

Journal

DATE	ACCOUNTS AND EXPLANATIONS	POST. REQ.	DEBIT	CREDIT

Req.2

Req. 1

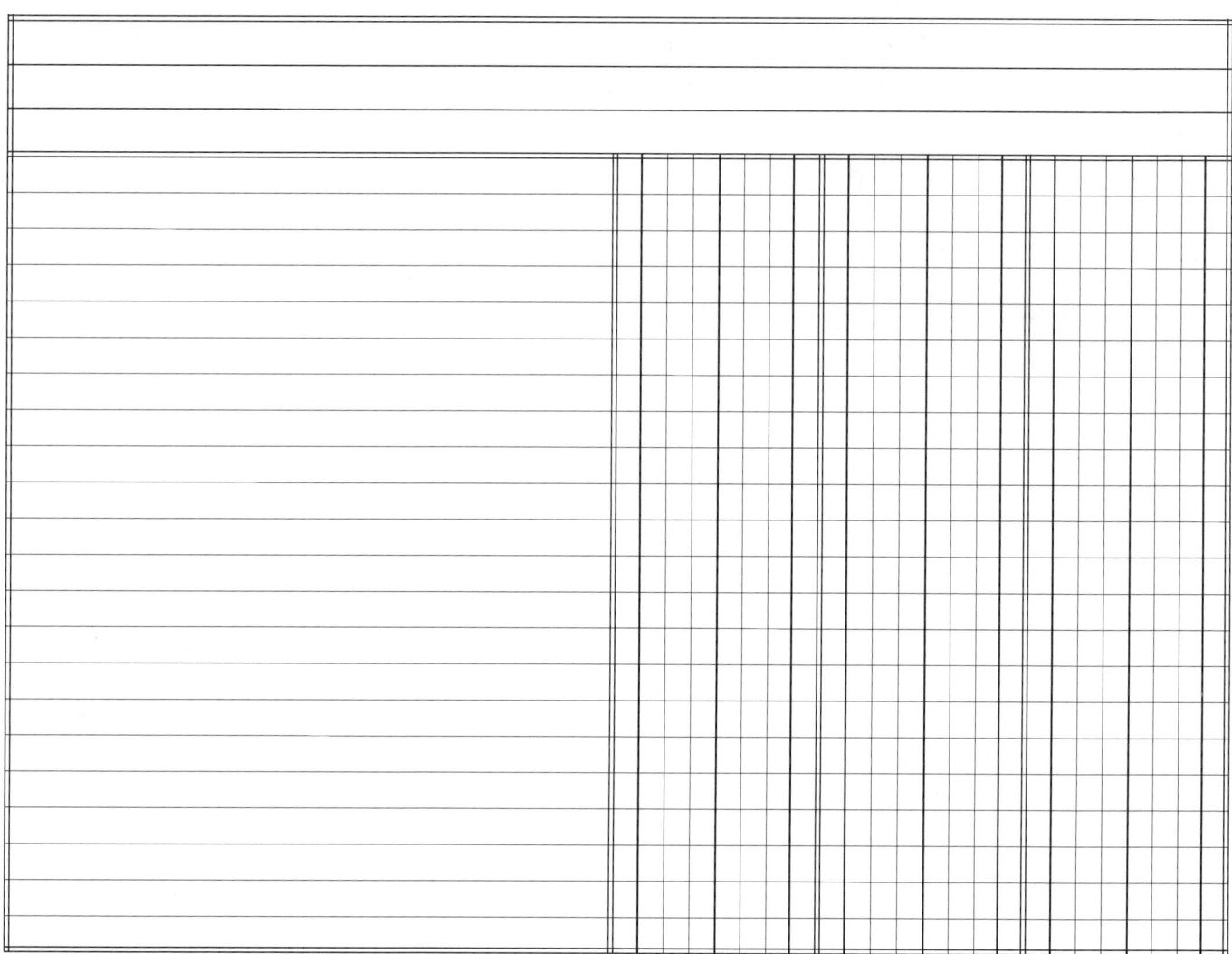

Req. 2

Req. 1

Req. 2

Req. 1

Req. 2

Req. 1

NAME
SECTION
DATE

Chapter 5

Decision Case 2

(Continued)

Req. 2

NAME
SECTION
DATE

Chapter 5

Decision Case 2

(Continued)

Req. 2

NAME
SECTION
DATE

Chapter 5

Decision Case 2

(Continued)

Req. 3

Req. 4

Ethical Issue

S6-1

S6-2

Journal					
DATE	ACCOUNTS AND EXPLANATIONS	POST. REF.	DEBIT		CREDIT

S6-3

S6-4

S6-6

S6-8

			POST. REF.	DEBIT	CREDIT
DATE	ACCOUNTS AND EXPLANATIONS				

Journal

S6-10

S6-12

S6-13

S6-14

Perpetual Inventory Record-FIFO

	Purchases			Cost of Goods Sold			Inventory on Hand		
Date	Quantity	Unit Cost	Total Cost	Quantity	Unit Cost	Total Cost	Quantity	Unit Cost	Total Cost

Ending inventory   =

Cost of goods sold   =

Journal					
DATE	ACCOUNTS AND EXPLANATIONS	POST. REF.	DEBIT		CREDIT

Perpetual Inventory Record-LIFO

		Purchases			Cost of Goods Sold			Inventory on Hand		
Date		Quantity	Unit Cost	Total Cost	Quantity	Unit Cost	Total Cost	Quantity	Unit Cost	Total Cost

Ending inventory =

Cost of goods sold =

Perpetual Inventory Record-Average Cost

		Purchases			Cost of Goods Sold			Inventory on Hand		
Date		Quantity	Unit Cost	Total Cost	Quantity	Unit Cost	Total Cost	Quantity	Unit Cost	Total Cost

Ending inventory   =

Cost of goods sold   =

Req. 1

	Journal			
DATE	ACCOUNTS AND EXPLANATIONS	POST. REF.	DEBIT	CREDIT

Req. 2

_____

_____

_____

_____

_____

_____

_____

_____

E6-7

_____

_____

_____

_____

_____

_____

_____

		Purchases			Cost of Goods Sold			Inventory on Hand		
Date		Quantity	Unit Cost	Total Cost	Quantity	Unit Cost	Total Cost	Quantity	Unit Cost	Total Cost

E6-9

a. _____

b. _____

c. _____

d. _____

_____

_____

e. _____

f. _____

_____

E6-12

E6-14

	20X2	20X1

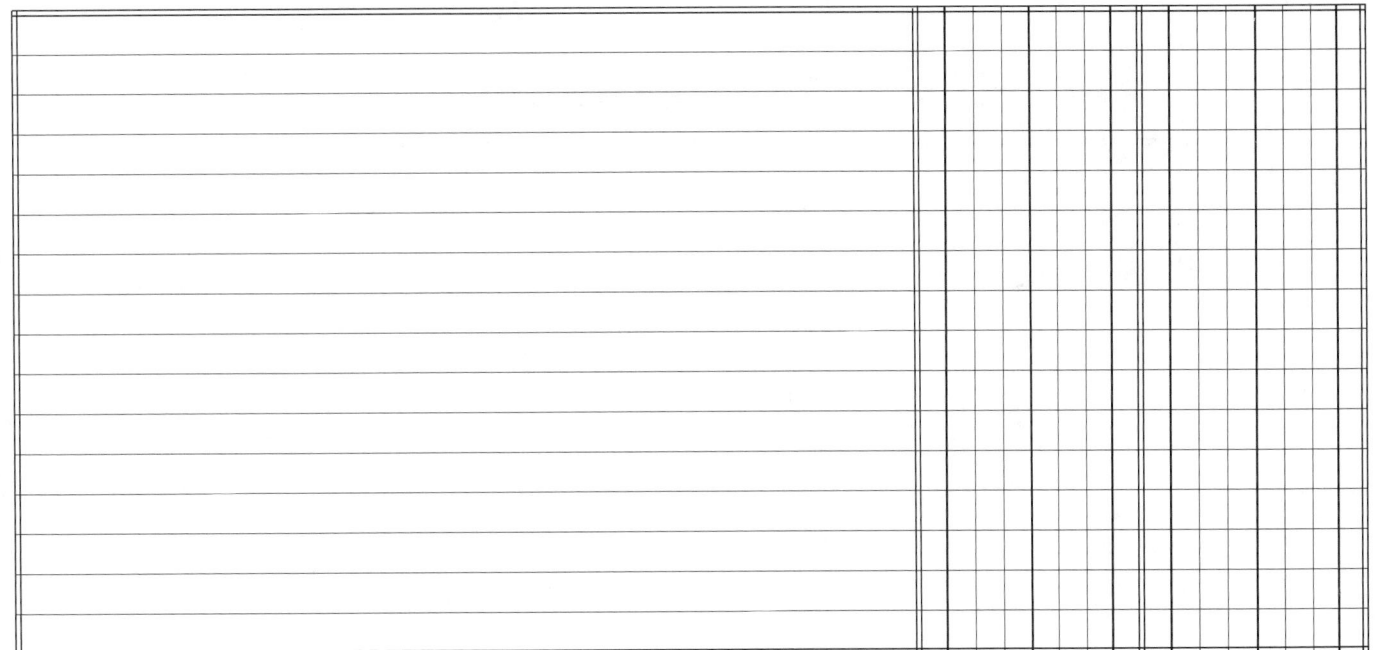

E6-16

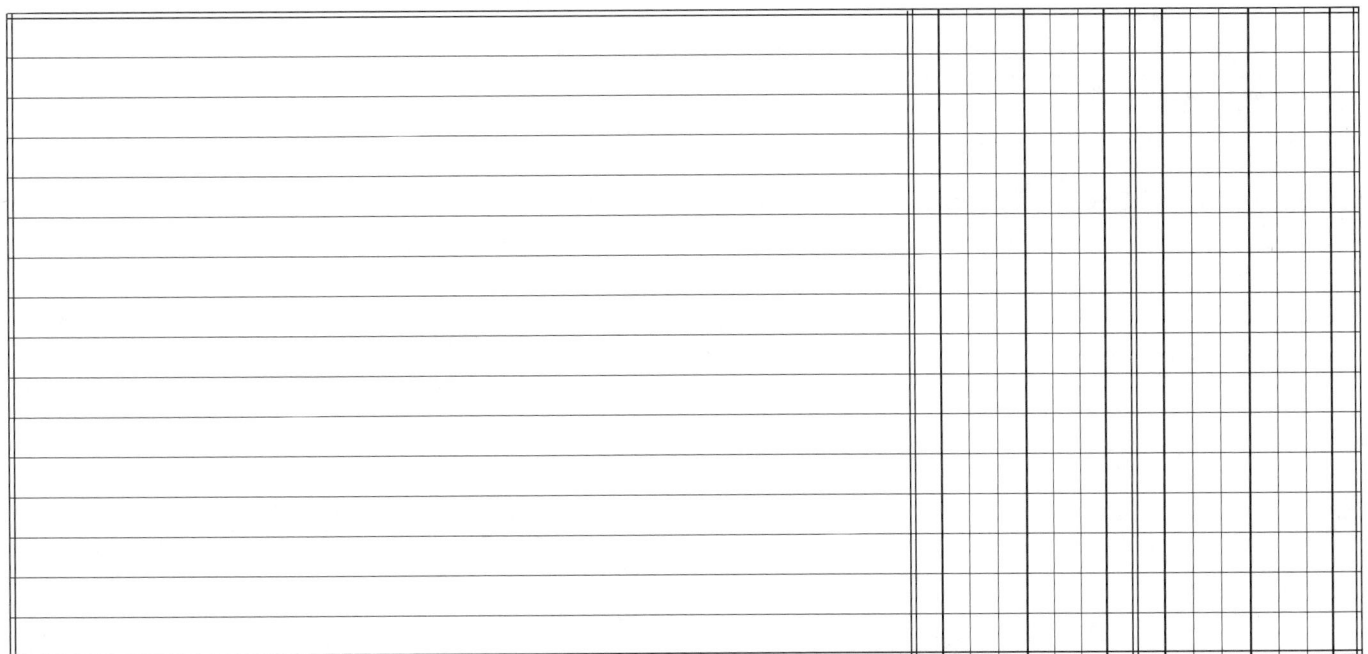

Req. 1

Perpetual Inventory Record-FIFO

CHAIR									
	Purchases			Cost of Goods Sold			Inventory on Hand		
Date	Quantity	Unit Cost	Total Cost	Quantity	Unit Cost	Total Cost	Quantity	Unit Cost	Total Cost

Ending inventory   =

Cost of goods sold   =

Req. 2

Journal

DATE		ACCOUNTS AND EXPLANATIONS	POST. REF.	DEBIT	CREDIT

Req. 1

Perpetual Inventory Record—Average Cost

CHAIR:									
	Purchases			Cost of Goods Sold			Inventory on Hand		
Date	Quantity	Unit Cost	Total Cost	Quantity	Unit Cost	Total Cost	Quantity	Unit Cost	Total Cost

Req. 2

Req. 1

Perpetual Inventory Record-LIFO

LAWN SUPPLIES									
	Purchases			Cost of Goods Sold			Inventory on Hand		
Date	Quantity	Unit Cost	Total Cost	Quantity	Unit Cost	Total Cost	Quantity	Unit Cost	Total Cost

Req. 2

Req. 3

Req. 1

Req. 2

Req. 3

Req. 1

Req. 2

Req. 1 (corrected income statements)

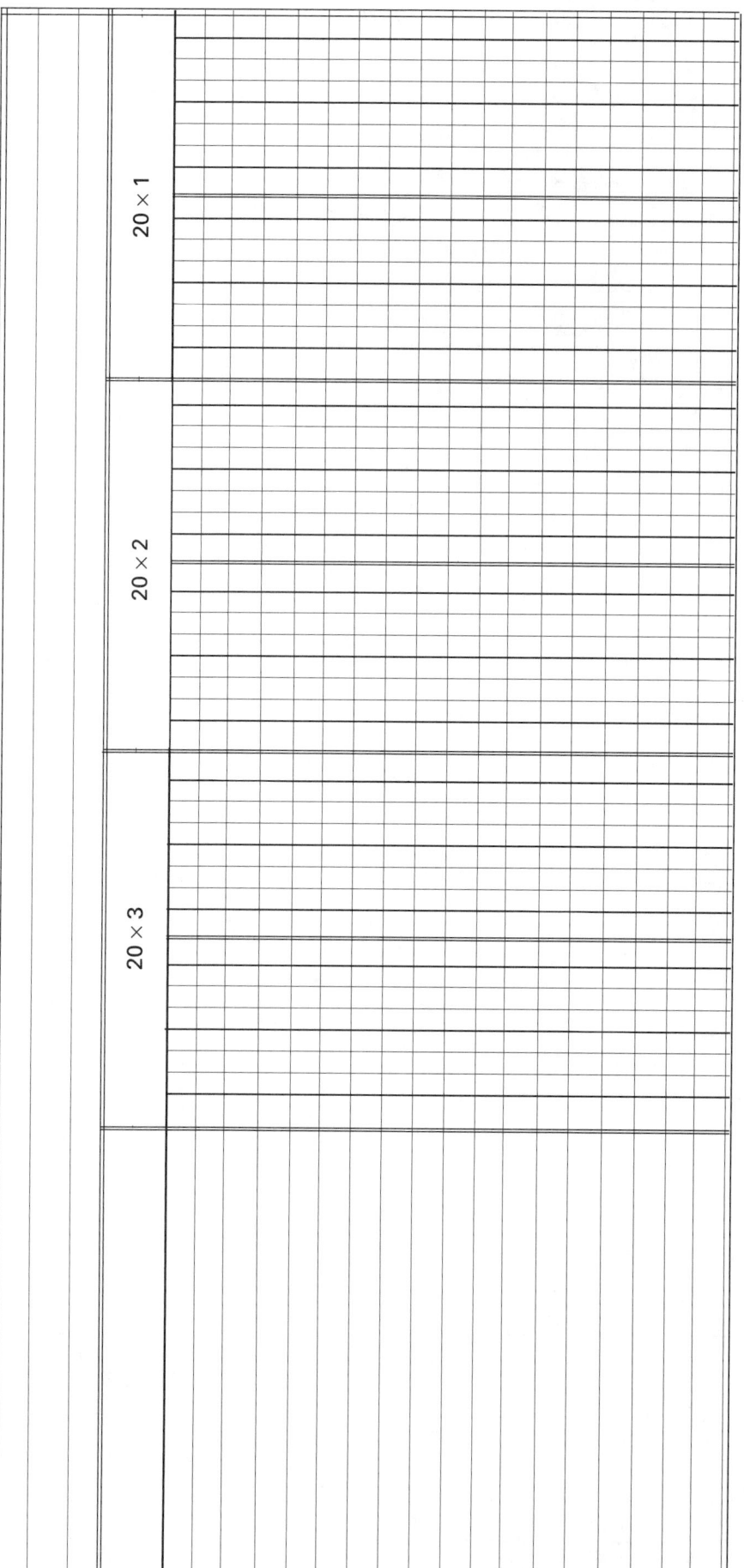

20 × 3 | 20 × 2 | 20 × 1

Req. 2 (net income effects of inventory errors)

Req. 1

Req. 2 (Income Statement through gross profit)

Req. 1

Perpetual Inventory Record-LIFO

TOYS									
		Purchases			Cost of Goods Sold			Inventory on Hand	
Date	Quantity	Unit Cost	Total Cost	Quantity	Unit Cost	Total Cost	Quantity	Unit Cost	Total Cost

Req. 2

Journal

DATE	ACCOUNTS AND EXPLANATIONS	POST. REF.	DEBIT	CREDIT

Req. 1

Perpetual Inventory Record—Average Cost

Date	Purchases			Cost of Goods Sold			Inventory on Hand		
	Quantity	Unit Cost	Total Cost	Quantity	Unit Cost	Total Cost	Quantity	Unit Cost	Total Cost

Req. 2

Req. 1

Perpetual Inventory Record—Average Cost

Date	Purchases			Cost of Goods Sold			Inventory on Hand		
	Quantity	Unit Cost	Total Cost	Quantity	Unit Cost	Total Cost	Quantity	Unit Cost	Total Cost

Req. 2

Req. 1

Req. 2

Req. 3

Req. 1

Req. 2

NAME
SECTION
DATE

Req. 1 (corrected income statements)

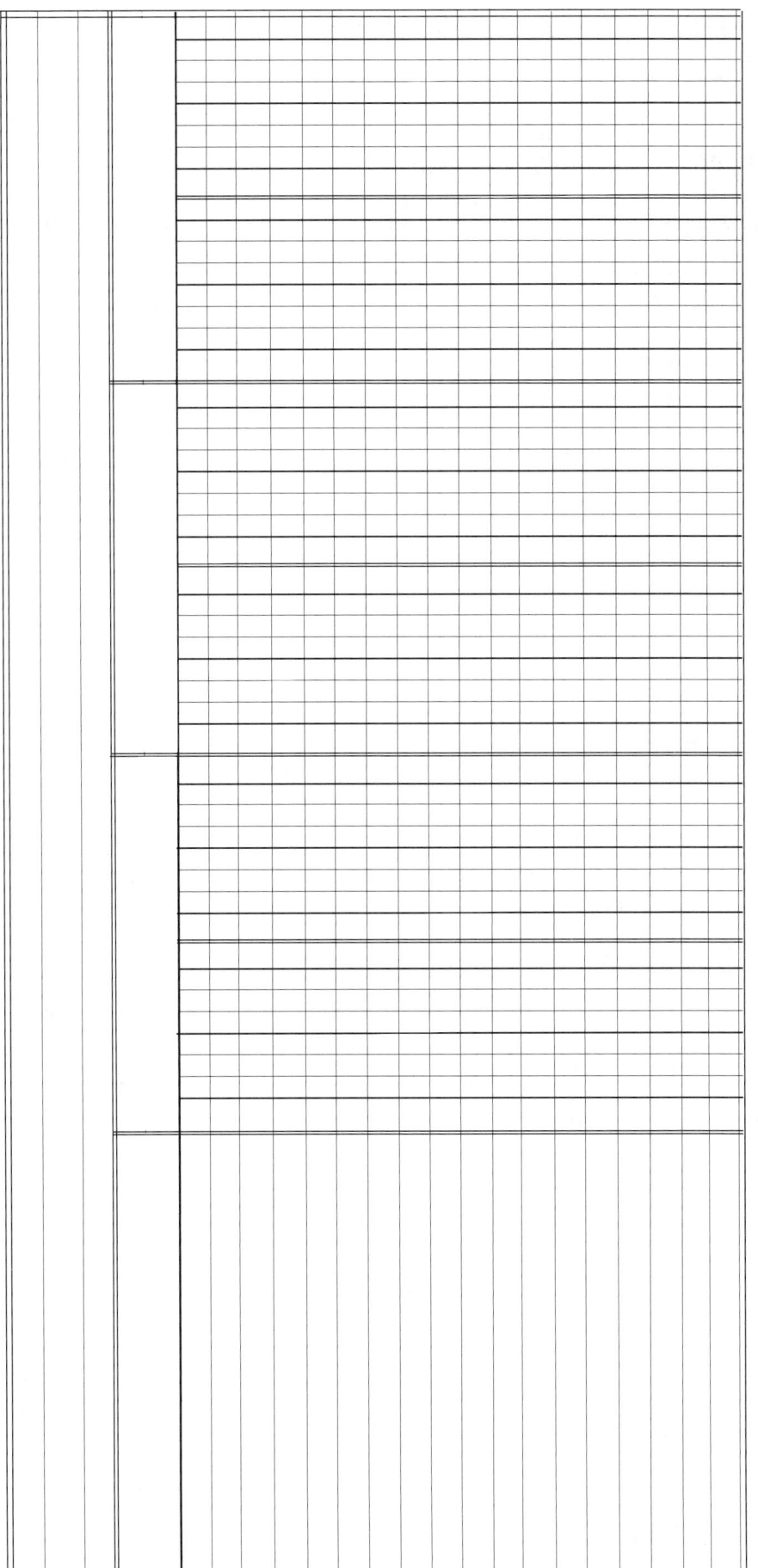

Req. 2

Req. 1 *(estimate of ending inventory by the gross profit method)*

Req. 2 (income statement through gross profit)

_____
_____
_____
_____
_____
_____
_____

S7-2

A. Software   —   Electronic linkages that allow different
B. Network   computers to share the same information
C. Server   —   Electronic equipment
D. Hardware   —   Programs that drive a computer
            —   Main computer in a networked system

S7-3

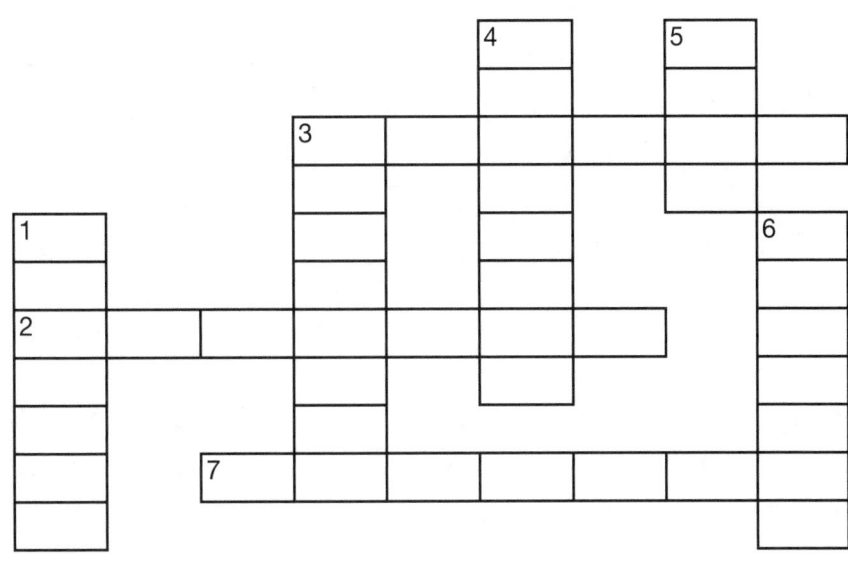

NUMBER   ACCOUNT

S7-5

j   =   General journal

S   =   Sales journal

CR   =   Cash receipts journal

P   =   Purchases journal

CP   =   Cash payments journal

Transactions:

—   a.   Cash sale of inventory
—   b.   Payment of rent
—   c.   Depreciation of computer equipment
—   d.   Purchases of inventory on account
—   e.   Collection of accounts receivable
—   f.   Expiration of prepaid insurance
—   g.   Sales on account
—   h.   Payment on account
—   i.   Cash purchase of inventory
—   j.   Collection of dividend revenue earned on an investment
—   k.   Prepayment of insurance
—   l.   Borrowing money on a long-term note payable
—   m.   Purchase of equipment on account
—   n.   Cost of goods sold along with a credit sale

S7-8

S7-10

S7-12

E7-2

E7-3

E7-4

E7-5

Cash Receipts Journal

PAGE

DATE	DEBITS			CREDITS			COST OF GOODS SOLD DR. INVENTORY CR.
	CASH	SALES DISCOUNTS	ACCOUNTS RECEIVABLE	SALES REVENUE	OTHER ACCOUNTS		
					ACCOUNT TITLE	POST REF.	AMOUNT

E7-7

Journal

DATE	ACCOUNTS AND EXPLANATIONS	POST. REF.	DEBIT	CREDIT

Purchases Journal

PAGE

DATE	ACCOUNT CREDITED	TERMS	POST. REF.	CREDITS	DEBITS		OTHER ACCOUNTS		
				ACCOUNTS PAYABLE	INVENTORY	SUPPLIES	ACCOUNT TITLE	POST. REF.	AMOUNT

Req. 1

ACCOUNT					ACCOUNT NO.		
						BALANCE	
DATE	ITEM	JRNL. REF.	DEBIT	CREDIT	DEBIT		CREDIT

ACCOUNT					ACCOUNT NO.		
						BALANCE	
DATE	ITEM	JRNL. REF.	DEBIT	CREDIT	DEBIT		CREDIT

ACCOUNT					ACCOUNT NO.		
						BALANCE	
DATE	ITEM	JRNL. REF.	DEBIT	CREDIT	DEBIT		CREDIT

ACCOUNT					ACCOUNT NO.		
						BALANCE	
DATE	ITEM	JRNL. REF.	DEBIT	CREDIT	DEBIT		CREDIT

Req. 2

ACCOUNT					ACCOUNT NO.			
		JRNL.				BALANCE		
DATE	ITEM	REF.	DEBIT	CREDIT	DEBIT		CREDIT	

ACCOUNT					ACCOUNT NO.			
		JRNL.				BALANCE		
DATE	ITEM	REF.	DEBIT	CREDIT	DEBIT		CREDIT	

ACCOUNT					ACCOUNT NO.			
		JRNL.				BALANCE		
DATE	ITEM	REF.	DEBIT	CREDIT	DEBIT		CREDIT	

Req. 3

Reqs. 1,2 and 3

Cash Payments Journal

PAGE

DATE	CK. NO.	ACCOUNT DEBITED	POST. REF.	DEBITS		CREDITS	
				OTHER ACCOUNTS	ACCOUNTS PAYABLE	INVENTORY	CASH

Kendrick Journal Entries

		Journal			PAGE
DATE		ACCOUNTS AND EXPLANATIONS	POST. REF.	DEBIT	CREDIT

Goodyear Journal Entries

		Journal			PAGE
DATE		ACCOUNTS AND EXPLANATIONS	POST. REF.	DEBIT	CREDIT

Reqs. 1–3

Reqs. 1 and 3

		Sales Journal				
DATE	INVOICE NO.	ACCOUNT DEBITED	POST. REF.	ACCOUNTS RECEIVABLE DR. SALES REVENUE CR.	COST OF GOODS SOLD DR. INVENTORY CR.	

NAME
SECTION
DATE

Cash Receipts Journal

PAGE _____

DATE	DEBITS		CREDITS				
	CASH	SALES DISCOUNTS	ACCOUNTS RECEIVABLE	SALES REVENUE	OTHER ACCOUNTS		
					ACCOUNT TITLE	POST REF.	AMOUNT	COST OF GOODS SOLD DR. INVENTORY CR.

Reqs. 1 and 3

Journal

DATE	ACCOUNTS AND EXPLANATIONS	POST. REF.	DEBIT	CREDIT

Req. 1

Req. 2

Req. 3 (Corrected Cash Receipts journal)

Cash Receipts Journal

PAGE ____

DATE	DEBITS			CREDITS				
	CASH	SALES DISCOUNTS	ACCOUNTS RECEIVABLE	SALES REVENUE	OTHER ACCOUNTS			COST OF GOODS SOLD DR. INVENTORY CR.
					ACCOUNT TITLE	POST REF.	AMOUNT	

Reqs. 1, 2 and 3

Purchases Journal

DATE	ACCOUNT CREDITED	TERMS	POST. REF.	CREDITS	DEBITS			
				ACCOUNTS PAYABLE	PURCHASES	INVENTORY	OTHER ACCOUNTS		
							ACCOUNT TITLE	POST. REF.	AMOUNT

Reqs. 1–3 (Continued)

Journal

DATE	ACCOUNTS AND EXPLANATIONS	POST. REF.	DEBIT	CREDIT

Reqs. 1–3 (Continued)

Cash Payments Journal

PAGE

DATE	CK. NO.	ACCOUNT DEBITED	POST. REF.	DEBITS		CREDITS	
				OTHER ACCOUNTS	ACCOUNTS PAYABLE	INVENTORY	CASH

Reqs. 1 and 4

GENERAL LEDGER

ACCOUNT						ACCOUNT NO.	
						BALANCE	
DATE	ITEM	JRNL. REF.	DEBIT	CREDIT		DEBIT	CREDIT

ACCOUNT						ACCOUNT NO.	
						BALANCE	
DATE	ITEM	JRNL. REF.	DEBIT	CREDIT		DEBIT	CREDIT

ACCOUNT						ACCOUNT NO.	
						BALANCE	
DATE	ITEM	JRNL. REF.	DEBIT	CREDIT		DEBIT	CREDIT

ACCOUNT						ACCOUNT NO.	
						BALANCE	
DATE	ITEM	JRNL. REF.	DEBIT	CREDIT		DEBIT	CREDIT

ACCOUNT						ACCOUNT NO.	
						BALANCE	
DATE	ITEM	JRNL. REF.	DEBIT	CREDIT		DEBIT	CREDIT

Reqs. 1 and 4 (Continued)

ACCOUNT INVENTORY					ACCOUNT NO.	
		JRNL.			BALANCE	
DATE	ITEM	REF.	DEBIT	CREDIT	DEBIT	CREDIT

ACCOUNT					ACCOUNT NO.	
		JRNL.			BALANCE	
DATE	ITEM	REF.	DEBIT	CREDIT	DEBIT	CREDIT

ACCOUNT					ACCOUNT NO.	
		JRNL.			BALANCE	
DATE	ITEM	REF.	DEBIT	CREDIT	DEBIT	CREDIT

ACCOUNT					ACCOUNT NO.	
		JRNL.			BALANCE	
DATE	ITEM	REF.	DEBIT	CREDIT	DEBIT	CREDIT

Reqs. 1 and 4 (Continued)

ACCOUNT						ACCOUNT NO.		
							BALANCE	
DATE	ITEM	JRNL. REF.	DEBIT	CREDIT		DEBIT		CREDIT

ACCOUNT						ACCOUNT NO.		
							BALANCE	
DATE	ITEM	JRNL. REF.	DEBIT	CREDIT		DEBIT		CREDIT

ACCOUNT						ACCOUNT NO.		
							BALANCE	
DATE	ITEM	JRNL. REF.	DEBIT	CREDIT		DEBIT		CREDIT

ACCOUNT						ACCOUNT NO.		
							BALANCE	
DATE	ITEM	JRNL. REF.	DEBIT	CREDIT		DEBIT		CREDIT

Reqs. 1 and 4 (Continued)

ACCOUNT						ACCOUNT NO.	
		JRNL.				BALANCE	
DATE	ITEM	REF.	DEBIT	CREDIT		DEBIT	CREDIT

ACCOUNT						ACCOUNT NO.	
		JRNL.				BALANCE	
DATE	ITEM	REF.	DEBIT	CREDIT		DEBIT	CREDIT

Reqs. 2 and 4

Accounts Receivable Subsidiary Ledger

ACCOUNT						ACCOUNT NO.		
							BALANCE	
DATE	ITEM	JRNL. REF.	DEBIT		CREDIT		DEBIT	CREDIT

ACCOUNT						ACCOUNT NO.		
							BALANCE	
DATE	ITEM	JRNL. REF.	DEBIT		CREDIT		DEBIT	CREDIT

ACCOUNT						ACCOUNT NO.		
							BALANCE	
DATE	ITEM	JRNL. REF.	DEBIT		CREDIT		DEBIT	CREDIT

Accounts Payable Subsidiary Ledger

ACCOUNT					ACCOUNT NO.	
					BALANCE	
DATE	ITEM	JRNL. REF.	DEBIT	CREDIT	DEBIT	CREDIT

ACCOUNT					ACCOUNT NO.	
					BALANCE	
DATE	ITEM	JRNL. REF.	DEBIT	CREDIT	DEBIT	CREDIT

ACCOUNT					ACCOUNT NO.	
					BALANCE	
DATE	ITEM	JRNL. REF.	DEBIT	CREDIT	DEBIT	CREDIT

Reqs. 3 and 5

Sales Journal						
DATE	INVOICE NO.	ACCOUNT DEBITED	POST. REF.	ACCOUNTS RECEIVABLE DR. SALES REVENUE CR.		COST OF GOODS SOLD DR. INVENTORY CR.

Req. 6

Chapter 7

P7-5A *(Continued)*

Cash Receipts Journal

PAGE

DATE	DEBITS			CREDITS					
	CASH	SALES DISCOUNTS	ACCOUNTS RECEIVABLE	SALES REVENUE	OTHER ACCOUNTS			COST OF GOODS SOLD DR. INVENTORY CR.
					ACCOUNT TITLE	POST REF.	AMOUNT	

P7-5A *(Continued)*

NAME
SECTION
DATE

Purchases Journal

DATE	ACCOUNT CREDITED	TERMS	POST. REF.	CREDITS	DEBITS			
				ACCOUNTS PAYABLE	INVENTORY	SUPPLIES	OTHER ACCOUNTS		
							ACCOUNT TITLE	POST. REF.	AMOUNT

NAME
SECTION
DATE

P7-5A *(Continued)*

Cash Payments Journal

PAGE

DATE	CK. NO.	ACCOUNT DEBITED	POST REF.	DEBITS		CREDITS	
				OTHER ACCOUNTS	ACCOUNTS PAYABLE	INVENTORY	CASH

Journal

DATE	ACCOUNTS AND EXPLANATIONS	POST. REF.	DEBIT	CREDIT

Reqs. 1 and 2

Row Number	Column	
	A	B
5		
6		
7		
8		
9		
10		
11		
12		
13		
14		
15		
16		
17		
18		
19		
20		

Req. 3

Reqs. 1,2, and 3

Sales Journal

DATE	INVOICE NO	ACCOUNT DEBITED	POST. REF.	ACCOUNTS RECEIVABLE DR. SALES REVENUE CR.	COST OF GOODS SOLD DR. INVENTORY CR.

Journal

DATE	ACCOUNTS AND EXPLANATIONS	POST. REF.	DEBIT	CREDIT

Reqs. 1,2, and 3 (Continued)

Cash Receipts Journal

	DEBITS				CREDITS				COST OF GOODS SOLD DR. INVENTORY CR.
						OTHER ACCOUNTS			PAGE
DATE	CASH	SALES DISCOUNTS	ACCOUNTS RECEIVABLE	SALES REVENUE	ACCOUNT TITLE	POST REF.	AMOUNT		

Req. 1

Req. 2

Req. 3 (Corrected cash Receipts journal)

Cash Receipts Journal

DATE	DEBITS			CREDITS				
	CASH	SALES DISCOUNTS	ACCOUNTS RECEIVABLE	SALES REVENUE	OTHER ACCOUNTS			COST OF GOODS SOLD DR. INVENTORY CR.
					ACCOUNT TITLE	POST REF.	AMOUNT	

PAGE

P7-4B

Reqs. 1,2,3

Purchases Journal

DATE	ACCOUNT CREDITED	TERMS	POST. REF.	CREDITS	DEBITS			OTHER ACCOUNTS		
				ACCOUNTS PAYABLE	INVENTORY	SUPPLIES	ACCOUNT TITLE	POST. REF.	AMOUNT	

Journal

DATE	ACCOUNTS AND EXPLANATIONS	POST. REF.	DEBIT	CREDIT

Reqs. 1,2,3 *(Continued)*

Cash Payments Journal

PAGE _____

DATE	CK. NO.	ACCOUNT DEBITED	POST. REF.	DEBITS		CREDITS	
				OTHER ACCOUNTS	ACCOUNTS PAYABLE	INVENTORY	CASH

Reqs. 1 and 4

GENERAL LEDGER

ACCOUNT					ACCOUNT NO.	
		JRNL. REF.			BALANCE	
DATE	ITEM		DEBIT	CREDIT	DEBIT	CREDIT

ACCOUNT					ACCOUNT NO.	
		JRNL. REF.			BALANCE	
DATE	ITEM		DEBIT	CREDIT	DEBIT	CREDIT

ACCOUNT					ACCOUNT NO.	
		JRNL. REF.			BALANCE	
DATE	ITEM		DEBIT	CREDIT	DEBIT	CREDIT

ACCOUNT					ACCOUNT NO.	
		JRNL. REF.			BALANCE	
DATE	ITEM		DEBIT	CREDIT	DEBIT	CREDIT

ACCOUNT	INVENTORY					ACCOUNT NO.	
		JRNL. REF.				BALANCE	
DATE	ITEM		DEBIT	CREDIT	DEBIT	CREDIT	

ACCOUNT						ACCOUNT NO.	
		JRNL. REF.				BALANCE	
DATE	ITEM		DEBIT	CREDIT	DEBIT	CREDIT	

ACCOUNT						ACCOUNT NO.	
		JRNL. REF.				BALANCE	
DATE	ITEM		DEBIT	CREDIT	DEBIT	CREDIT	

ACCOUNT						ACCOUNT NO.	
		JRNL. REF.				BALANCE	
DATE	ITEM		DEBIT	CREDIT	DEBIT	CREDIT	

ACCOUNT					ACCOUNT NO.		
						BALANCE	
DATE	ITEM	JRNL. REF.	DEBIT	CREDIT	DEBIT	CREDIT	

ACCOUNT					ACCOUNT NO.		
						BALANCE	
DATE	ITEM	JRNL. REF.	DEBIT	CREDIT	DEBIT	CREDIT	

ACCOUNT					ACCOUNT NO.		
						BALANCE	
DATE	ITEM	JRNL. REF.	DEBIT	CREDIT	DEBIT	CREDIT	

ACCOUNT					ACCOUNT NO.		
						BALANCE	
DATE	ITEM	JRNL. REF.	DEBIT	CREDIT	DEBIT	CREDIT	

ACCOUNT						ACCOUNT NO.			
						BALANCE			
DATE	ITEM	JRNL. REF.	DEBIT		CREDIT	DEBIT		CREDIT	

ACCOUNT						ACCOUNT NO.			
						BALANCE			
DATE	ITEM	JRNL. REF.	DEBIT		CREDIT	DEBIT		CREDIT	

Reqs. 2 and 4

Accounts Receivable Subsidiary Ledger

ACCOUNT					ACCOUNT NO.			
						BALANCE		
DATE	ITEM	JRNL. REF.	DEBIT	CREDIT		DEBIT		CREDIT

ACCOUNT					ACCOUNT NO.			
						BALANCE		
DATE	ITEM	JRNL. REF.	DEBIT	CREDIT		DEBIT		CREDIT

ACCOUNT					ACCOUNT NO.			
						BALANCE		
DATE	ITEM	JRNL. REF.	DEBIT	CREDIT		DEBIT		CREDIT

Accounts Payable Subsidiary Ledger

ACCOUNT						ACCOUNT NO.	
						BALANCE	
DATE	ITEM	JRNL. REF.	DEBIT	CREDIT		DEBIT	CREDIT

ACCOUNT						ACCOUNT NO.	
						BALANCE	
DATE	ITEM	JRNL. REF.	DEBIT	CREDIT		DEBIT	CREDIT

ACCOUNT						ACCOUNT NO.	
						BALANCE	
DATE	ITEM	JRNL. REF.	DEBIT	CREDIT		DEBIT	CREDIT

Reqs. 3 and 5

		Sales Journal					
DATE	INVOICE NO	ACCOUNT DEBITED	POST. REF.	ACCOUNTS RECEIVABLE DR. SALES REVENUE CR.		COST OF GOODS SOLD DR. INVENTORY CR.	

Req. 6

Chapter 7

P7-5B *(Continued)*

PAGE

Cash Receipts Journal

DATE	DEBITS			CREDITS			
	CASH	SALES DISCOUNTS	ACCOUNTS RECEIVABLE	SALES REVENUE	OTHER ACCOUNTS		COST OF GOODS SOLD DR. INVENTORY CR.
					ACCOUNT TITLE	POST REF.	AMOUNT

Purchases Journal

DATE	ACCOUNT CREDITED	TERMS	POST. REF.	CREDITS	DEBITS			OTHER ACCOUNTS		
				ACCOUNTS PAYABLE	INVENTORY	SUPPLIES		ACCOUNT TITLE	POST. REF.	AMOUNT

NAME
SECTION
DATE

Cash Payments Journal

DATE	CK. NO.	ACCOUNT DEBITED	POST. REF.	DEBITS		CREDITS	
				OTHER ACCOUNTS	ACCOUNTS PAYABLE	INVENTORY	CASH

PAGE

Journal

DATE	ACCOUNTS AND EXPLANATIONS	POST. REF.	DEBIT	CREDIT

Sales Journal

DATE	INVOICE NO.	ACCOUNT DEBITED	POST. REF.	ACCOUNTS RECEIVABLE DR. SALES REVENUE CR.

Cash Receipts Journal

DATE	DEBITS			CREDITS			
	CASH	SALES DISCOUNTS	ACCOUNTS RECEIVABLE	SALES REVENUE	OTHER ACCOUNTS		
					ACCOUNT TITLE	POST REF.	AMOUNT

NAME
SECTION
DATE

Chapter 7

Decision Case 1

(Continued)

Decision Case 2

Reqs. 1–3

NAME
SECTION
DATE

Chapter 7

Team Project 1

(Continued)

NAME
SECTION
DATE

Chapter 7

Team Project 2

(Continued)

NAME
SECTION
DATE

Chapter 7

**Excel Application
Exercise**

Comprehensive Problem

Reqs. 1,3, & 5

ACCOUNT					ACCOUNT NO.	
					BALANCE	
DATE	ITEM	JRNL. REF.	DEBIT	CREDIT	DEBIT	CREDIT

ACCOUNT					ACCOUNT NO.	
					BALANCE	
DATE	ITEM	JRNL. REF.	DEBIT	CREDIT	DEBIT	CREDIT

ACCOUNT					ACCOUNT NO.	
					BALANCE	
DATE	ITEM	JRNL. REF.	DEBIT	CREDIT	DEBIT	CREDIT

NAME
SECTION
DATE

Chapters 1–7

Comprehensive
Problem (Continued)

Reqs. 1,3, & 5 (Continued)

ACCOUNT						ACCOUNT NO.			
							BALANCE		
DATE	ITEM	JRNL. REF.	DEBIT		CREDIT		DEBIT		CREDIT

ACCOUNT						ACCOUNT NO.			
							BALANCE		
DATE	ITEM	JRNL. REF.	DEBIT		CREDIT		DEBIT		CREDIT

ACCOUNT						ACCOUNT NO.			
							BALANCE		
DATE	ITEM	JRNL. REF.	DEBIT		CREDIT		DEBIT		CREDIT

ACCOUNT						ACCOUNT NO.			
							BALANCE		
DATE	ITEM	JRNL. REF.	DEBIT		CREDIT		DEBIT		CREDIT

Reqs. 1,3, & 5 (Continued)

ACCOUNT					ACCOUNT NO.		
						BALANCE	
DATE	ITEM	JRNL. REF.	DEBIT	CREDIT	DEBIT		CREDIT

ACCOUNT					ACCOUNT NO.		
						BALANCE	
DATE	ITEM	JRNL. REF.	DEBIT	CREDIT	DEBIT		CREDIT

ACCOUNT					ACCOUNT NO.		
						BALANCE	
DATE	ITEM	JRNL. REF.	DEBIT	CREDIT	DEBIT		CREDIT

ACCOUNT					ACCOUNT NO.		
						BALANCE	
DATE	ITEM	JRNL. REF.	DEBIT	CREDIT	DEBIT		CREDIT

Reqs. 1,3, & 5 (Continued)

ACCOUNT					ACCOUNT NO.	
DATE	ITEM	JRNL. REF.	DEBIT	CREDIT	BALANCE	
					DEBIT	CREDIT

ACCOUNT					ACCOUNT NO.	
DATE	ITEM	JRNL. REF.	DEBIT	CREDIT	BALANCE	
					DEBIT	CREDIT

ACCOUNT					ACCOUNT NO.	
DATE	ITEM	JRNL. REF.	DEBIT	CREDIT	BALANCE	
					DEBIT	CREDIT

ACCOUNT					ACCOUNT NO.	
DATE	ITEM	JRNL. REF.	DEBIT	CREDIT	BALANCE	
					DEBIT	CREDIT

Reqs. 1,3, & 5 (Continued)

ACCOUNT					ACCOUNT NO.	
		JRNL. REF.			BALANCE	
DATE	ITEM		DEBIT	CREDIT	DEBIT	CREDIT

ACCOUNT					ACCOUNT NO.	
		JRNL. REF.			BALANCE	
DATE	ITEM		DEBIT	CREDIT	DEBIT	CREDIT

ACCOUNT					ACCOUNT NO.	
		JRNL. REF.			BALANCE	
DATE	ITEM		DEBIT	CREDIT	DEBIT	CREDIT

ACCOUNT					ACCOUNT NO.	
		JRNL. REF.			BALANCE	
DATE	ITEM		DEBIT	CREDIT	DEBIT	CREDIT

NAME
SECTION
DATE

Chapters 1–7

Comprehensive
Problem (Continued)

Reqs. 1,3, & 5 (Continued)

ACCOUNT					ACCOUNT NO.	
		JRNL.			BALANCE	
DATE	ITEM	REF.	DEBIT	CREDIT	DEBIT	CREDIT

ACCOUNT					ACCOUNT NO.	
		JRNL.			BALANCE	
DATE	ITEM	REF.	DEBIT	CREDIT	DEBIT	CREDIT

ACCOUNT					ACCOUNT NO.	
		JRNL.			BALANCE	
DATE	ITEM	REF.	DEBIT	CREDIT	DEBIT	CREDIT

ACCOUNT					ACCOUNT NO.	
		JRNL.			BALANCE	
DATE	ITEM	REF.	DEBIT	CREDIT	DEBIT	CREDIT

Reqs. 1,3, & 5 (Continued)

ACCOUNT					ACCOUNT NO.	
					BALANCE	
DATE	ITEM	JRNL. REF.	DEBIT	CREDIT	DEBIT	CREDIT

Reqs. 1 & 3   Accounts Receivable Subsidary Ledger

ACCOUNT							ACCOUNT NO.	
							BALANCE	
DATE	ITEM	JRNL. REF.	DEBIT		CREDIT		DEBIT	CREDIT

ACCOUNT							ACCOUNT NO.	
							BALANCE	
DATE	ITEM	JRNL. REF.	DEBIT		CREDIT		DEBIT	CREDIT

ACCOUNT							ACCOUNT NO.	
							BALANCE	
DATE	ITEM	JRNL. REF.	DEBIT		CREDIT		DEBIT	CREDIT

ACCOUNT							ACCOUNT NO.	
							BALANCE	
DATE	ITEM	JRNL. REF.	DEBIT		CREDIT		DEBIT	CREDIT

NAME
SECTION
DATE

Chapters 1–7

Comprehensive
Problem *(Continued)*

Reqs. 1 & 3 (Continued)   Accounts Payable Subsidary Ledger

ACCOUNT					ACCOUNT NO.		
						BALANCE	
DATE	ITEM	JRNL. REF.	DEBIT	CREDIT	DEBIT	CREDIT	

ACCOUNT					ACCOUNT NO.		
						BALANCE	
DATE	ITEM	JRNL. REF.	DEBIT	CREDIT	DEBIT	CREDIT	

ACCOUNT					ACCOUNT NO.		
						BALANCE	
DATE	ITEM	JRNL. REF.	DEBIT	CREDIT	DEBIT	CREDIT	

ACCOUNT					ACCOUNT NO.		
						BALANCE	
DATE	ITEM	JRNL. REF.	DEBIT	CREDIT	DEBIT	CREDIT	

Req. 2

		Sales Journal				
DATE	INVOICE NO	ACCOUNT DEBITED	POST. REF.	ACCOUNTS RECEIVABLE DR. SALES REVENUE CR.		COST OF GOODS SOLD DR. INVENTORY CR.

Comprehensive Problem *(Continued)*

Cash Receipts Journal

PAGE

DATE	DEBITS			CREDITS				
	CASH	SALES DISCOUNTS	ACCOUNTS RECEIVABLE	SALES REVENUE	OTHER ACCOUNTS ACCOUNT TITLE	POST REF.	AMOUNT	Cost of Goods sold DR Inventory CR

Chapters 1–7

Comprehensive
Problem *(Continued)*

Purchases Journal

DATE	ACCOUNT CREDITED	TERMS	POST. REF.	CREDITS	DEBITS		DEBITS		
				ACCOUNTS PAYABLE	INVENTORY	SUPPLIES	OTHER ACCOUNTS		
							ACCOUNT TITLE	POST. REF.	AMOUNT

Comprehensive Problem *(Continued)*

Cash Payments Journal

PAGE

DATE	CK. NO.	ACCOUNT DEBITED	POST. REF.	DEBITS — OTHER ACCOUNTS	DEBITS — ACCOUNTS PAYABLE	CREDITS — INVENTORY	CREDITS — CASH

Req. 5

Journal				
DATE	ACCOUNTS AND EXPLANATIONS	POST. REF.	DEBIT	CREDIT

NAME
SECTION
DATE

Chapters 1–7

Comprehensive
Problem*(Continued)*

Req. 5 (continued)

Journal

DATE		ACCOUNTS AND EXPLANATIONS	POST. REF.	DEBIT	CREDIT

Req. 4

Digital Meter Company
Work Sheet
Year Ended December 31, 20XX

ACCOUNT TITLES	UNADJUSTED TRIAL BALANCE		ADJUSTMENTS		ADJUSTED TRIAL BALANCE		INCOME STATEMENT		BALANCE SHEET	
	DEBIT	CREDIT	DEBIT	CREDIT	DEBIT	CREDIT	DEBIT	CREDIT	DEBIT	CREDIT

Req. 4 (Continued)

Digital Meter Company

Work Sheet

Year Ended December 31, 20XX

ACCOUNT TITLES	UNADJUSTED TRIAL BALANCE		ADJUSTMENTS		ADJUSTED TRIAL BALANCE		INCOME STATEMENT		BALANCE SHEET	
	DEBIT	CREDIT	DEBIT	CREDIT	DEBIT	CREDIT	DEBIT	CREDIT	DEBIT	CREDIT

S8-2

DATE														

S8-8

		Journal					
DATE		ACCOUNTS AND EXPLANATIONS	POST. REF.	DEBIT		CREDIT	

S8-12

_____
_____
_____
_____
_____
_____
_____
_____
_____
_____
_____

E8-4

a. _____   e. _____

b. _____   f. _____

c. _____   g. _____

d. _____   h. _____

Req. 1

		Journal				
DATE		ACCOUNTS AND EXPLANATIONS	POST. REF.	DEBIT		CREDIT

E8-8

Req. 1

		Journal			
DATE		ACCOUNTS AND EXPLANATIONS	POST. REF.	DEBIT	CREDIT

Req. 2

Req. 1

_____

_____

_____

_____

_____

_____

_____

_____

_____

_____

Req. 2

		Journal			
DATE		ACCOUNTS AND EXPLANATIONS	POST. REF.	DEBIT	CREDIT

Req. 3

Requirement 1	Requirement 2	Requirement 3
Missing Internal Control Characteristic	Possible Problem	Solution
A. Firewalls and Encryption	Data could fall into the wrong hands.	Incorporate these into the computer
B. Competent Personnel	Loss of revenue, Lawsuit	Allow the paraprofessionals to do only the work they know
C. Separation of Duties	Theft, Embezzlement	Have separate duties - 3 people
D. Assignment of Responsibilities	Lost revenue	Hire someone to manage others, or assign 1 person
E. Separation of Duties / Assigned Responsibilities	Theft	Separate duties - 2

NAME
SECTION
DATE

Chapter 8

pg. 333

P8-3A

Silver Maple Art Gallery					
Bank Reconciliation					
April 30, 2004					
Bank					
Balance, April 30, 2004					18102
Add:					1397
Deposits in transit (1,060 + 337 = 1397)					19499
Less:					
Outstanding checks					
No. 3119			432		
No. 3120		1675			
No. 3121			100		
No. 3122 Add all checks together		2413			(4820)
Adjusted bank balance on April 30, 2004 (19499 - 4820 = 14679)					14679
Book					
Balance, April 30, 2004					13659
Add:					
Bank Collection (BC) - Bank collection of a note receivable		1300			
EFT collection of rent			300		
Book error (1430 - 1390 = 540)			540		
Add all together					2140
Less:					
EFT payment of insurance			200		
Service Charge			20		
Unauthorized-signature check (US)			900		
Add all together					(1120)
Adjusted book balance on April 30, 2004 (13659 + 2140 = 15799 - 1120 = 14679)					14679

Req. 1

Stop'n'Shop Food Mart						
Bank Reconciliation						
August 31, 2004						
Bank						
Balance, Aug. 31, 2004 (J.)					7527.	22
Add:						
Deposit of Aug. 31 of transit (H.)					316	15
					7843	37
Less:						
Outstanding Checks (D) (46.10 + 141.00 + 578.05 + 11.87 + 609.51 + 8.88 + 101.63 =	1497	04				
1497.04)						
Correction of bank error which credited our account for the deposit of another company (I)	300				(1797	04
Adjusted bank balance, Aug. 31, 2004					6046	33
Book						
Balance, Aug. 31, 2004 (A)					6409	31
Add:						
Bank collection of a note receivable including interest - interest 191.00 (E)	1191					
Interest Revenue earned on bank balance (F)	38.	19				
Add up					1229	19
Less:						
EFT - Rent + Insurance (750 + 290 = 1040) (C)	1040					
Service charge of 10.00 (G)	10					
Returned check due to an unauthorized signature 395.00 (B)	395					
NSF check 147.17 (B)	147	17				
Add up					(1592	17)
Adjusted book balance on Aug. 31, 2004 (6409.31 + 1229.19 - 1592.17 = 6046.33)					6046	33

Req. 2

Journal

DATE		ACCOUNTS AND EXPLANATIONS	POST. REF.	DEBIT	CREDIT
Aug.	31	Cash		1191	
		Note Receivable			1000
		Interest Revenue			191
Aug.	31	Cash		38^{19}	
		Interest Revenue			38^{19}
Aug.	31	Rent Expense		750	
		Cash			750
Aug.	31	Insurance Expense		290	
		Cash			290
Aug.	31	Misc. Expense		10	
		Cash			10
Aug.	31	Accounts Receivable for Lakeland Express		395	
		Accounts Receivable for Veracruz, Inc.		147^{17}	
		Cash (395 + 147.17 = 542.17)			542^{17}

Req. 1

_____
_____
_____
_____
_____
_____
_____
_____

Req. 2

_____
_____
_____
_____

Req. 3

	Journal			
DATE	ACCOUNTS AND EXPLANATIONS	POST. REF.	DEBIT	CREDIT

_____
_____

Req. 3 and 4

		Journal			
DATE		ACCOUNTS AND EXPLANATIONS	POST. REF.	DEBIT	CREDIT

Req. 4

		Journal			
DATE		ACCOUNTS AND EXPLANATIONS	POST. REF.	DEBIT	CREDIT

Req. 1

Req. 2

		Journal			
DATE		ACCOUNTS AND EXPLANATIONS	POST. REF.	DEBIT	CREDIT

Journal

DATE	ACCOUNTS AND EXPLANATIONS	POST. REF.	DEBIT	CREDIT

Req. 3

		Journal				
DATE		ACCOUNTS AND EXPLANATIONS	POST. REF.	DEBIT		CREDIT

NAME
SECTION
DATE

Chapter 8

Decision Case 1

(Continued)

Reqs. 1 and 2

NAME
SECTION
DATE

Chapter 8

Financial Statement Case

Reqs. 1–5

NAME

SECTION

DATE

Team Project

Team Project
(Continued)

Chapter 8

Excel Application Exercise

S9-2

S9-3

S9-5

Journal

DATE	ACCOUNTS AND EXPLANATIONS	POST. REF.	DEBIT	CREDIT

S9-8

	Journal			
DATE	ACCOUNTS AND EXPLANATIONS	POST. REF.	DEBIT	CREDIT

S9-10

		Journal			
DATE		ACCOUNTS AND EXPLANATIONS	POST. REF.	DEBIT	CREDIT

S9-11

		Journal			
DATE		ACCOUNTS AND EXPLANATIONS	POST. REF.	DEBIT	CREDIT

A. CURRENT RATIO =

B. DEBT RATIO =

C. GROSS PROFIT PERCENTAGE =

D. RATE OF INVENTORY TURNOVER =

Req. 1

		Journal			
DATE	ACCOUNTS AND EXPLANATIONS		POST. REF.	DEBIT	CREDIT

Req. 2

Req. 1

	Journal			
DATE	ACCOUNTS AND EXPLANATIONS	POST. REF.	DEBIT	CREDIT

Req. 2

Req. 1

		Journal			
DATE		ACCOUNTS AND EXPLANATIONS	POST. REF.	DEBIT	CREDIT

Req. 2

Journal

DATE	ACCOUNTS AND EXPLANATIONS	POST. REF.	DEBIT	CREDIT

Reqs. 1–3

Journal

DATE	ACCOUNTS AND EXPLANATIONS	POST. REF.	DEBIT	CREDIT

Journal

DATE	ACCOUNTS AND EXPLANATIONS	POST. REF.	DEBIT	CREDIT

Journal

DATE	ACCOUNTS AND EXPLANATIONS	POST. REF.	DEBIT	CREDIT

Req. 1

Req. 2

Req. 1

Req. 2

Req. 1 (Allowance Method)

DATE		ACCOUNTS AND EXPLANATIONS	POST. REF.	DEBIT	CREDIT
June	30	Accounts Receivable		5 6 0 0 0 0	
		Sales Revenue			5 6 0 0 0 0
June	30	Cash		5 6 7 4 0 0	
		Accounts Receivable			5 6 7 4 0 0
June	30	Uncollectible - Account Expense (560,000 × 0.02 = 11,200)		1 1 2 0 0	
		Allowance for Uncollectible Accounts			1 1 2 0 0
June	30	Allowance for Uncollectible Accounts		8 9 0 0	
		Accounts Receivable			8 9 0 0

Journal

pg. 366
pg. 368

Accounts Receivable

210,000 Balance	
560,000	567,400
	8,900
193,700 Balance	

Uncollectible Account Expenses

11,200
11,200 Balance

Allowance for Uncollectible Accounts

	2,800 Balance
	11,200
8,900	
	5,100 Balance

Req. 2 (Direct Write-Off Method)

			DATE	ACCOUNTS AND EXPLANATIONS	POST. REF.	DEBIT	CREDIT
Journal							
	June	30		Accounts Receivable		560000	
				Sales Revenue			560000
	June	30		Cash		567400	
				Accounts Receivable			567400
	June	30		Uncollectible - Account Expense		8900	
				Accounts Receivable			8900

Account Receivable

210,000 Balance	
560,000	567,400
	8,400
143,700 Balance	

Uncollectible Account Expense

| 8,900 | |
| 8,900 Balance | |

Req. 3

_____

_____

_____

_____

_____

_____

_____

_____

_____

Req. 4

_____

_____

_____

_____

_____

_____

_____

_____

_____

_____

_____

_____

_____

Req. 1

		Journal				
DATE		ACCOUNTS AND EXPLANATIONS	POST. REF.	DEBIT	CREDIT	
Aug.	9	Allowance for Uncollectible Accounts		1000		
		Accounts Receivable — J. Aguilar			200	
		Accounts Receivable — Seaton Co.			100	
		Accounts Receivable — T. Taylor			700	
Sept.	30	Uncollectible - Account Expense (140,000 x 0.15 = 2100)		2100		
		Allowance for Uncollectible Accounts			2100	
Oct	18	Allowance for Uncollectible Accounts		900		
		Accounts Receivable — Lintz Co.			500	
		Accounts Receivable — Navisor Corp.			400	
Dec.	31	Uncollectible - Account Expense		300		
		Allowance for Uncollectible Accounts			300	

$$100,000 \times 0.001 = 100 \quad +$$
$$40,000 \times 0.005 = 200 \quad +$$
$$14,000 \times 0.05 = 700 \quad +$$
$$9,000 \times 0.3 = 2700 = 3,700$$

Req. 2

ACCOUNT	ALLOWANCE FOR UNCOLLECTABLE ACCOUNTS			BALANCE	
DATE	ITEM	DEBIT	CREDIT	DEBIT	CREDIT
June 30	Balance				3 2 0 0
Aug. 9	Write-off	1,000			2 2 0 0
Sept. 30			2,100		4 3 0 0
Oct 18		900			3 4 0 0
Dec. 31			300		

Req. 3

Reqs. 1 and 2

ACCOUNT		**ALLOWANCE FOR UNCOLLECTABLE ACCOUNTS**					
		JRNL.				BALANCE	
DATE	ITEM	REF.	DEBIT	CREDIT		DEBIT	CREDIT

ACCOUNT		**UNCOLLECTABLE-ACCOUNT EXPENSE**					
		JRNL.				BALANCE	
DATE	ITEM	REF.	DEBIT	CREDIT		DEBIT	CREDIT

Req. 2 (Continued)

		Journal			
DATE		ACCOUNTS AND EXPLANATIONS	POST. REF.	DEBIT	CREDIT

Req. 3

Simple Interest = Principal · Rate · Time

$I = P \cdot r \cdot t$

Req. 1

NOTE	DUE DATE	PRINCIPAL + INTEREST		MATURITY VALUE
(1)	Dec. 23, 2009	$13,000 \times 0.09 \times 1 = 1,170 + 13,000$	=	14,170
(2)	May 30, 2009	$12,000 \times 0.12 \times 6/12 (0.5) = 720 + 12,000$	=	12,720
(3)	Jan. 6, 2009	$9,000 \times 0.1 \times 30/360 = 75 + 9,000$	=	9,075

or

$$\frac{9,000 \times 0.1 \times 30}{360}$$

Req. 2

Journal

DATE		ACCOUNTS AND EXPLANATIONS	POST. REF.	DEBIT	CREDIT
Dec.	31	Interest Receivable (26 + 120 + 60 = 206)		206	
		Interest Revenue			206

Dec. 23 $13,000 \times 0.09 \times 8/360 = 26$ accrued interest revenue on 1st note

Nov. 30 $12,000 \times 0.12 \times 30/360 = 120$ accrued interest revenue on 2nd note

Dec. 7 $9,000 \times 0.1 \times 24/360 = 60$ accrued interest revenue on 3rd note

$$30/360 = 1/12$$

Req. 3

Journal

DATE		ACCOUNTS AND EXPLANATIONS	POST. REF.	DEBIT	CREDIT
Dec.	31	Cash (from above)		14170	
		Interest Receivable (from above) 8 days			26
		Interest Revenue (360 - 8 = 352 $13,000 \times 0.09 \times 352/360 = 1144$)			1144
		Note Receivable			13000

Req. 2

Reqs. 1 and 2

ACCOUNT		**ALLOWANCE FOR DOUBTFUL ACCOUNTS**					
						BALANCE	
DATE	ITEM	JRNL. REF.	DEBIT	CREDIT	DEBIT	CREDIT

ACCOUNT		**UNCOLLECTIBLE-ACCOUNT EXPENSE**					
						BALANCE	
DATE	ITEM	JRNL. REF.	DEBIT	CREDIT	DEBIT	CREDIT

Req. 2

Journal

DATE	ACCOUNTS AND EXPLANATIONS	POST. REF.	DEBIT	CREDIT

Journal

DATE	ACCOUNTS AND EXPLANATIONS	POST. REF.	DEBIT	CREDIT

Journal

DATE	ACCOUNTS AND EXPLANATIONS	POST. REF.	DEBIT	CREDIT

Journal

DATE	ACCOUNTS AND EXPLANATIONS	POST. REF.	DEBIT	CREDIT

Req. 1

DOLLAR AMOUNTS IN MILLIONS

20 × 8   **20 × 7**

A. CURRENT RATIO:

B. ACID TEST RATIO:

C. ONE DAY'S SALES:

**DAYS' SALES IN AVERAGE
RECEIVABLES:**

Req. 2

Req. 1

_____
_____
_____
_____
_____
_____
_____

Req. 2

_____
_____
_____
_____
_____
_____
_____
_____

Req. 1

NAME
SECTION
DATE

Chapter 9

Decision Case 2

(Continued)

Req. 2

Chapter 9

Ethical Issue

NAME
SECTION
DATE

Chapter 9

**Financial
Statement Case**

Reqs. 1–3

Chapter 9

Team Project

NAME
SECTION
DATE

Chapter 9

Team Project

(Continued)

NAME
SECTION
DATE

Chapter 9

Team Project
(Continued)

Req. 2

Journal

DATE	ACCOUNTS AND EXPLANATIONS	POST. REF.	DEBIT	CREDIT

Req. 1

NOTE	DUE DATE	PRINCIPAL + INTEREST		MATURITY VALUE
(1)	_____	_____	=	_____
(2)	_____	_____	=	_____
(3)	_____	_____	=	_____

Req. 2

NOTE	MATURITY VALUE	DISCOUNT	PROCEEDS
(1)	_____	_____	_____
(2)	_____	_____	_____
(3)	_____	_____	_____

Req. 3

Journal

DATE	ACCOUNTS AND EXPLANATIONS	POST. REF.	DEBIT	CREDIT

Journal

DATE	ACCOUNTS AND EXPLANATIONS	POST. REF.	DEBIT	CREDIT

Req. 1

		Journal				
DATE		ACCOUNTS AND EXPLANATIONS	POST. REF.	DEBIT	CREDIT	

Req. 2

Reqs. 1 & 2

1. A. $\dfrac{42,000,000 - 4,000,000}{5}$ = 7,200,000

2, 3. $\dfrac{42,000,000 - 4,000,000}{4,000,000}$ 6 per mile   6 × 750,000 = 4,500,000

3. C. 42,000,000 × 0.4 = 16,800,000

DDB = 2 × straight line

2. 42,000,000 - 7,200,000 = 34,800,000

Req. 1

Req. 2

S10-7

Journal

DATE	ACCOUNTS AND EXPLANATIONS	POST. REF.	DEBIT	CREDIT

Req. 1

		Journal			
DATE		ACCOUNTS AND EXPLANATIONS	POST. REF.	DEBIT	CREDIT

S10-10

Req. 1

_____

_____

_____

_____

_____

Req. 2

		Journal			
DATE		ACCOUNTS AND EXPLANATIONS	POST. REF.	DEBIT	CREDIT

Req. 1

Req. 2

DATE		ACCOUNTS AND EXPLANATIONS	POST. REF.	DEBIT	CREDIT
Journal					

S10-12

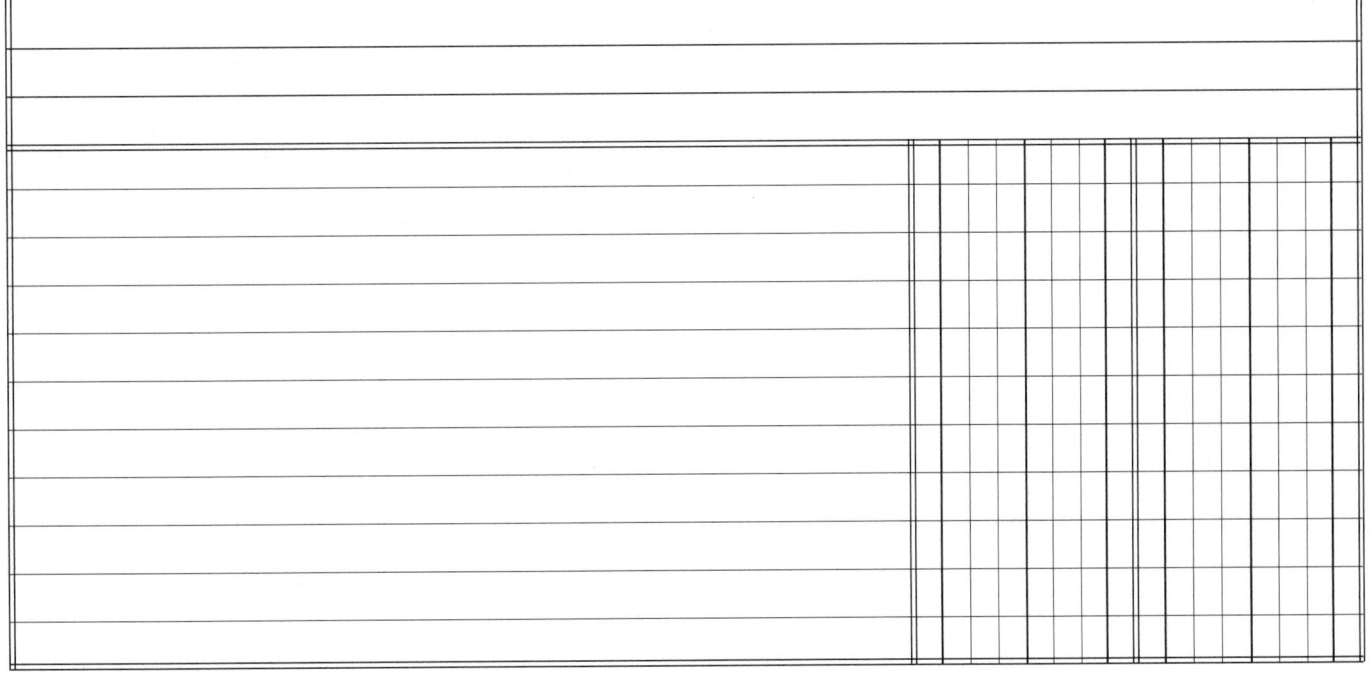

E10-2

Req. 1

Req. 2

		Journal				
DATE		ACCOUNTS AND EXPLANATIONS	POST. REF.	DEBIT		CREDIT

		Journal			
DATE		ACCOUNTS AND EXPLANATIONS	POST. REF.	DEBIT	CREDIT

E10-4

A. Capital Expenditure

B. Expense

C. Capital Expenditure

D. Expense

E. Capital Expenditure

F. Capital Expenditure

G. Capital Expenditure

H. Capital Expenditure

I. Capital Expenditure

J. Expense

Journal

DATE	ACCOUNTS AND EXPLANATIONS	POST. REF.	DEBIT	CREDIT

Journal

DATE	ACCOUNTS AND EXPLANATIONS	POST. REF.	DEBIT	CREDIT

E10-11

		Journal			
DATE		ACCOUNTS AND EXPLANATIONS	POST. REF.	DEBIT	CREDIT

Journal

DATE	ACCOUNTS AND EXPLANATIONS	POST. REF.	DEBIT	CREDIT

Req. 1

_____

_____

_____

_____

_____

_____

_____

_____

Req. 2

		Journal			
DATE		ACCOUNTS AND EXPLANATIONS	POST. REF.	DEBIT	CREDIT

_____

_____

_____

_____

_____

_____

_____

_____

_____

_____

_____

_____

_____

E10-15

		Journal			
DATE		ACCOUNTS AND EXPLANATIONS	POST. REF.	DEBIT	CREDIT

Req. 1

ITEM	LAND	LAND IMPROVEMENTS	SALES BUILDING	FURNITURE
(a)				
(b)				
(c)				
(d)				
(e)				
(f)				
(g)				
(h)				
(i)				
(j)				
(k)				
(l)				
(m)				
(n)				
(o)				
(p)				
(q)				
Totals				

Req. 2

		Journal			
DATE		ACCOUNTS AND EXPLANATIONS	POST. REF.	DEBIT	CREDIT

Journal

DATE	ACCOUNTS AND EXPLANATIONS	POST. REF.	DEBIT	CREDIT

NAME
SECTION
DATE

P10-4A

Req. 1

Straight-Line Depreciation Schedule

Date	Asset Cost	Depreciation Rate	Depreciable Cost	Depreciation Amount	Accumulated Depreciation	Asset Book Value	
Jan. 3, 2004 (124,000 + 700+100 +12,100 + 3,100 = 240,000) - Cost	240000	20% or 1/5	220000		44000	240000	
Dec. 31, 2004		20% or 1/5	220000	44000	44000	196000	Move up 1 line
Dec. 31, 2005		20% or 1/5	220000	44000	88000	152000	
Dec. 31, 2006		20% or 1/5	220000	44000	132000	108000	
Dec. 31, 2007		20% or 1/5	220000	44000	176000	64000	
Dec. 31, 2008		20% or 1/5	220000	44000	220000	20000	

add 44,000   subtract 44,000

COMPUTATIONS:

Asset Cost -

Dep. Rate - 240,000 × 1/5 =

Dep. Cost - 240,000 - 20,000 = 220,000

P10-4A (Continued)

Req. 1 (Continued) Units-of-Production Depreciation Schedule

Date	Asset Cost	Depreciation per Unit	Number of Units	Depreciation Amount	Accumulated Depreciation	Asset Book Value
Jan. 3, 2004	240000					240000
Dec. 31, 2004		1.10	50000	55000	55000	185000
Dec. 31, 2005		1.10	45000	49500	104500	135500
Dec. 31, 2006		1.10	40000	44000	148500	91500
Dec. 31, 2007		1.10	35000	38500	187000	53000
Dec. 31, 2008		1.10	30000	33000	220000	20000

COMPUTATIONS:

$$\text{Dep per unit} = \frac{240,000 - 20,000}{200,000} = \frac{220,000}{200,000} = \$1.10$$

$$1.10 \times 50,000 = 55,000$$
$$240,000 - 55,000 = 185,000$$

$$1.10 \times 45,000 = 49,500 + 55,000 = 104,500$$
$$240,000 - 104,500 = 135,500$$

Req. 1 (Continued) Double-Declining-Balance Depreciation Schedule

Date	Asset Cost	DDB Rate	X	Book Value	=	Depreciation Amount	Accumulated Depreciation	Asset Book Value
Jan 3, 2004	240000							240000
Dec 31, 2004		40%		240000		96000	96000	144000
Dec 31, 2005		40%		144000		57600	153600	86400
Dec 31, 2006		40%		86400		34560	188160	51840
Dec 31, 2007		40%		51840		20736	208896	31104
Dec 31, 2008		40%		31104		11104	220000	20000

COMPUTATIONS:

DDB rate - 5 years = 20% × 2 = 40%

240,000 × 0.4 = 96,000

240,000 - 96,000 = 144,000

19,407

Req. 2

Double-Declining-Balance — Most depreciation in the first year

Straight Line — Least depreciation in the first year

Part 1

Req. 1

Journal

DATE	ACCOUNTS AND EXPLANATIONS	POST. REF.	DEBIT	CREDIT
	Assets (Cash, Receivables, Inventory, Plant Assets)		2700000	
	Goodwill		2500000	
	Liabilities			2200000
	Cash			3000000

3,000,000 - Net asset acquired (2,700,000 - 2,200,000 = 1,500,000) then

3,000,000 - 500,000 = 2,500,000

Req. 2 - pg. 417

Refer to 417

Part 2

Req. 1

Journal

DATE	ACCOUNTS AND EXPLANATIONS	POST. REF.	DEBIT	CREDIT
	Coal		2 800 000	
	Cash			28 00 000
	Coal		6 0 000	
	Cash			6 0 000
	Coal		4 5 000	
	Cash			4 5 000
	Coal		3 0 000	
	Note Payable			3 0 000
			1 1 7 4 000	
	Depletion Expense		1 1 7 4 000	1 1 7 4 000
	Accumulated Depletion of Coal			1 1 7 4 000
	(2,800,000 +60,000 + 45,000 + 30,000 = 2,935,000)			
	2,935,000 ÷ 100,000 = 29.35			
	29.35 × 40,000 = 1,174,000			
	Accounts Receivable (40,000 × 39 = 1,560,000)		1 560 000	
	Sales Revenue			1 560 000
	Operating Expense		2 52 000	
	Cash			2 52 000

Req. 2

	Georgia - Pacific's Corp.		
	Income Statement - Coal Operations		
	Year 1		
Sales Revenue		1 560 000	1 560 000
Depletion Expense		1 1 7 4 000	
Operating Expense		2 52 000	1 4 26 000
Net Income			1 3 4 000

Reqs. 1–3

1. Balance Sheet at Dec. 31, 2002

    Property, Plant, Equipment   9,000,000   9.0

      Less - Accumulated Depreciation   (3,100,000)   (3.1)

    Property, Plant, Equipment (book value)   5,900,000   5.9 billion

2. Assets - Liabilities = Owner's Equity

    Total Assets at Dec. 31, 2002   24.5

    Total Liabilities at Dec. 31, 2002   (12.7)

      Owner's Equity   11.8 billion

3. Total Revenues - Total Expenses = Net Income

    Total Revenues for 2002   20.2

    Total Expenses for 2002   (17.1)

      Net Income   3.1 billion

Req. 1

ITEM	LAND	LAND IMPROVEMENTS	APARTMENT BUILDING	FURNITURE

COMPUTATIONS:

Req. 2

		Journal			
DATE	ACCOUNTS AND EXPLANATIONS	POST. REF.	DEBIT	CREDIT	

Journal

DATE	ACCOUNTS AND EXPLANATIONS	POST. REF.	DEBIT	CREDIT

		Journal				
DATE		ACCOUNTS AND EXPLANATIONS	POST. REF.	DEBIT	CREDIT	

Req. 1

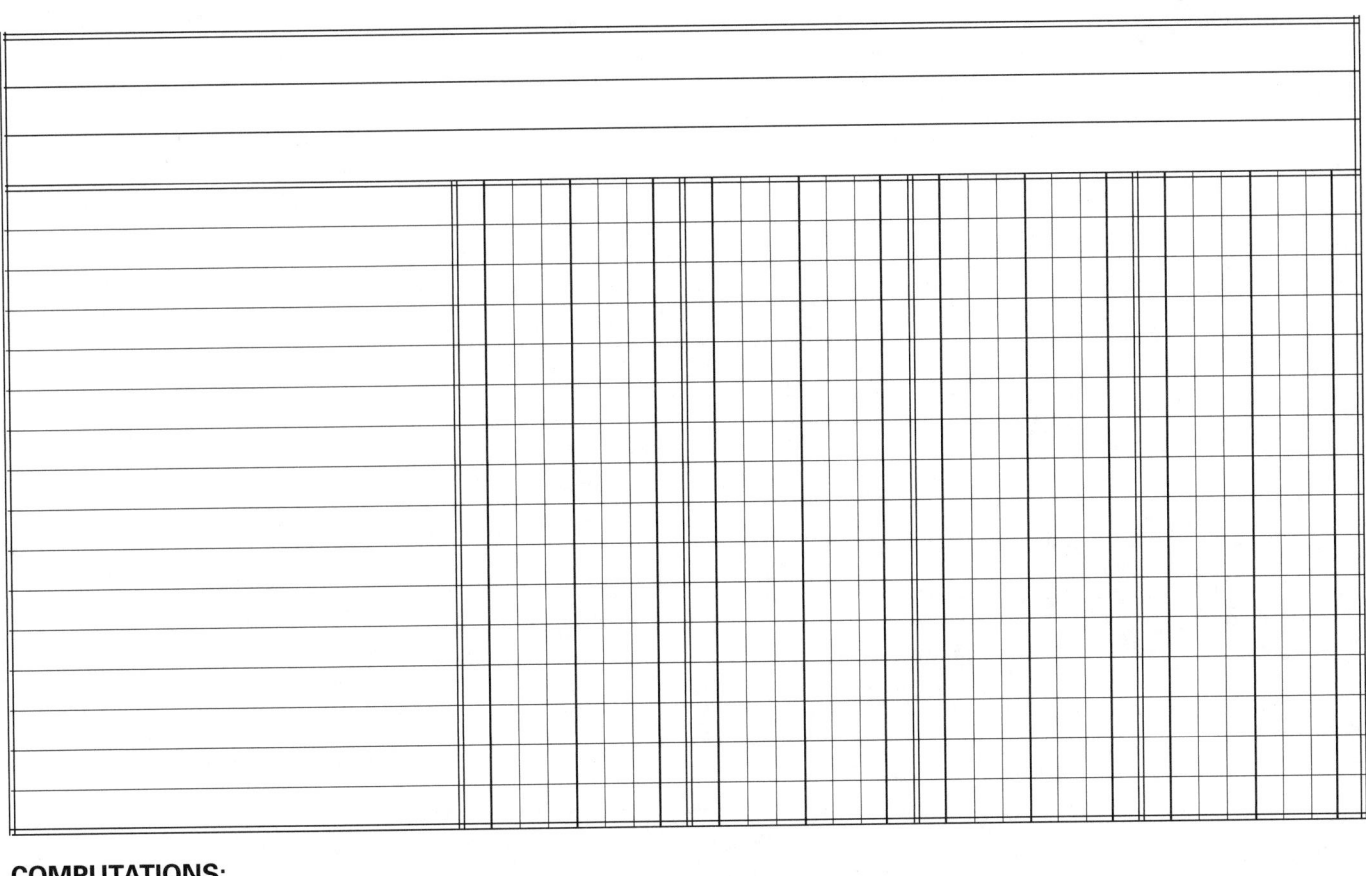

COMPUTATIONS:

NAME
SECTION
DATE

Chapter 10

Decision Case 1

(Continued)

Req. 2

NAME
SECTION
DATE

Chapter 10

Decision Case 1

(Continued)

Chapter 10

Decision Case 2

Reqs. a–c

Req. 1

Req. 2

NAME
SECTION
DATE

Chapter 10

**Financial
Statement Case**

Reqs. 1–3

Chapter 10

Excel Application
Exercise

Reqs. 1–3

Reqs. 1–3 (Continued)

Journal

DATE	ACCOUNTS AND EXPLANATIONS	POST. REF.	DEBIT	CREDIT

Req. 1

		Journal	POST. REF.	DEBIT	CREDIT
DATE		ACCOUNTS AND EXPLANATIONS			

Req. 2

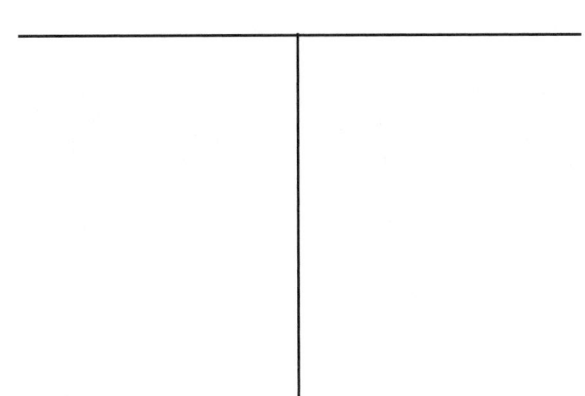

S11-5

S11-7

Reqs. a–c

		Journal			
DATE		ACCOUNTS AND EXPLANATIONS	POST. REF.	DEBIT	CREDIT

S11-10

S11-12

		Journal			
DATE		ACCOUNTS AND EXPLANATIONS	POST. REF.	DEBIT	CREDIT

Journal

DATE	ACCOUNTS AND EXPLANATIONS	POST. REF.	DEBIT	CREDIT

Req. 1

		Journal			
DATE		ACCOUNTS AND EXPLANATIONS	POST. REF.	DEBIT	CREDIT

Req. 2

Journal

DATE	ACCOUNTS AND EXPLANATIONS	POST. REF.	DEBIT	CREDIT

Req. a

Req. b

Journal

DATE	ACCOUNTS AND EXPLANATIONS	POST. REF.	DEBIT	CREDIT

	Journal			
DATE	ACCOUNTS AND EXPLANATIONS	POST. REF.	DEBIT	CREDIT

Journal

DATE	ACCOUNTS AND EXPLANATIONS	POST. REF.	DEBIT	CREDIT

Journal

DATE		ACCOUNTS AND EXPLANATIONS	POST. REF.	DEBIT	CREDIT
2005					
Feb.	3	Equipment		10000	
		Note Payable - Short-term			10000
Feb.	28	Cash (51,000 × $^1/_3$ = 17,000 × 1.05 = 17,850)		17850	
		Accounts Receivable (51,000 × $^2/_3$ = 34000 × 1.05 = 35700)		35700	
		Sales Revenue			51000
		Sales Tax Payable (17850 + 35700 = 53550 - 51000 = 2550			2550
		or 51000 × 0.05 = 2550)			
Mar.	7	Sales Tax Payable		2550	
		Cash			2550
April	30	Cash		100000	
		Note Payable - Long-term			100000
Aug.	30	Note Payable		10000	
		Interest Expense (10,000 × 0.09 = 900 × $^6/_{12}$ = 450)		450	
		Cash			10450
Nov.	30	Inventory		7200	
		Note Payable - Short-term			7200
Dec.	31	Warranty Expense (260,000 × 0.03 = 7800)		7800	
		Estimated Warranty Payable			7800
Dec.	31	Interest Expense (100,000 × 0.09 = 9,000 × $^8/_{12}$ = 6000)		6000	
		Interest Payable			6000
Dec.	31	Interest Expense (7200 × 0.08 = 576 × $^1/_{12}$ = 48)		48	
		Interest Payable			48
2006					
Feb.	28	Note Payable - Short-term		7200	
		Interest Payable (from above)		48	
		Interest Expense (7200 × 0.08 = 576 × $^2/_{12}$ = 96		96	
		Cash (7200 + 48 + 96 = 7344)			7344

over

		Journal														
DATE		ACCOUNTS AND EXPLANATIONS	POST. REF.			DEBIT						CREDIT				
April	30	Interest Payable (from above)				6	0	0	0							
		Interest Expense (100,000 x 0.09 = 36,000 x 4/12 = 3000)				3	0	0	0							
		Cash											9	0	0	0

Req. 1

18880 + 64813 = 83,693	c.	Total employee earnings
83,693 - 5109 = 78,584	a.	Straight-time earnings
78,584 + 5109 = 83,693	j.	Salary expense
18880 - 1373 - 6052 - 9293 = 2162	f.	Charitable contributions

Req. 2

	Journal																
DATE	ACCOUNTS AND EXPLANATIONS	POST. REF.			DEBIT							CREDIT				
	Salary Expense																
	Salary Expense				8	3	6	9	3								
	Employee Income Tax Payable												9	2	9	3
	FICA Tax Payable												6	0	5	2
	Employee Charitable Contributions Payable												2	1	6	2
	Employee Medical Insurance Payable												1	3	7	3
	Salary Payable to Employees												6	4	8	1	3

Req. 1

Employee Jan Summers			
For the Year ended Dec. 31, 2005			
Gross Pay 66500×12 = 78000			
Salary earnings (66500×12 = 78000)	78000		
Bonus (78,000 × 0.15 = 11700)	11700		
Gross Pay		89700	
Deductions			
Federal Income Tax (820×12 = 9840 + 2,480 = 12,320)	12320		
State Income Tax (60×12 = 720 + 80 = 800)	800		
FICA Tax (87,000 × 0.08 = 6960)	6960		
United Fund Contribution (89,700 × 0.01 = 897)	897		
Life Insurance (20×12 = 240)	240		
Total Deductions (Add all up)		21217	
Net Pay			
Net Pay (89700 - 21217 = 68483)			68483

Req. 2

Gross Pay	89,700
Employer Payroll Taxes :	
FICA Tax	6960
State Unemployment Tax (7000 × 0.054 = 378)	378
Federal Unemployment Tax (7000 × 0.008 = 56)	56
Benefits :	
Health Insurance (40×12 = 480)	480
Pension Benefits	4,000
Total Annual Cost of Employee (Add all up)	101,574

Req. 3

		Journal				
DATE		ACCOUNTS AND EXPLANATIONS	POST. REF.	DEBIT	CREDIT
a.		Employee's Total Earnings :			
		Salary Expense		78 000	
		Bonus Program		11 700	
		Employee Federal Income Tax Payable			12 320
		Employee State Income Tax Payable			800
		FICA Tax Payable			6 960
		Employee Contributions to United Way			897
		Employee Life Insurance			240
		Cash			68 483
b.		Employer Payroll Taxes :			
		Payroll Tax Expense (↓ added up)			
		FICA Tax Payable		7 394	6 960
		State Unemployment Tax			378
		Federal Unemployment Tax			56
c.		Employer Cost of Employee Benefits :			
		Health Insurance Expense		480	
		Pension Expense		4 000	
		Employee Benefits Payable			4 480

Reqs. 1 & 2

ACCOUNT								ACCOUNT NO.			
									BALANCE		
DATE		ITEM	JRNL. REF.	DEBIT		CREDIT		DEBIT		CREDIT	

ACCOUNT								ACCOUNT NO.			
									BALANCE		
DATE		ITEM	JRNL. REF.	DEBIT		CREDIT		DEBIT		CREDIT	

ACCOUNT								ACCOUNT NO.			
									BALANCE		
DATE		ITEM	JRNL. REF.	DEBIT		CREDIT		DEBIT		CREDIT	

ACCOUNT								ACCOUNT NO.			
									BALANCE		
DATE		ITEM	JRNL. REF.	DEBIT		CREDIT		DEBIT		CREDIT	

Reqs. 1 & 2 (Continued)

ACCOUNT					ACCOUNT NO.	
		JRNL. REF.			BALANCE	
DATE	ITEM		DEBIT	CREDIT	DEBIT	CREDIT

ACCOUNT					ACCOUNT NO.	
		JRNL. REF.			BALANCE	
DATE	ITEM		DEBIT	CREDIT	DEBIT	CREDIT

ACCOUNT					ACCOUNT NO.	
		JRNL. REF.			BALANCE	
DATE	ITEM		DEBIT	CREDIT	DEBIT	CREDIT

ACCOUNT					ACCOUNT NO.	
		JRNL. REF.			BALANCE	
DATE	ITEM		DEBIT	CREDIT	DEBIT	CREDIT

Req. 2

		Journal			
DATE		ACCOUNTS AND EXPLANATIONS	POST. REF.	DEBIT	CREDIT

Req. 3

Reqs. 1 and 3

EMPLOYEE NAME	HRS.	GROSS PAY			DEDUCTIONS				NET PAY	
		STRAIGHT-TIME	OVERTIME	TOTAL	FED INCOME TAX	FICA	HEALTH INS.	TOTAL	AMOUNT	CHECK NO.
1. Clay Cooper	43	400	45	445	74	36	16	126	319	
2. Tim LeMann	44	480	108	588	90	47	10	147	441	
3. Lana Marx	48	1,400	420	1820	319	64	46	429	1391	
4. Karen York	40	240	0	240	32	19	6	57	163	
	177	2520	573	2433	515	166	78	759	2334	

3093

COMPUTATIONS:

$\underset{\text{per hour}}{\downarrow}$ $\quad$ $\underset{\text{overtime}}{\downarrow}$ $\quad$ $\underset{\text{Total}}{\downarrow}$

1. $400 \div 40 = 10 \times 1.5 = 35 \times 15 = 45 \quad + 400 = 445 \qquad 74+36+16 = 126 \qquad 445 \times 0.08 = 36 \qquad 445-126 = 319$

2. $480 \div 40 = 12 \qquad 6 \times 18 = 108 + 480 = 588 \qquad 90+47+10 = 147 \qquad 588 \times 0.08 = 47 \qquad 588-147 = 441$

3. $1,400 \div 40 = 35 \qquad 8 \times 62.5 = 420 \qquad 630 \qquad 319+64+46 = 429 \qquad 800 \times 0.08 = 64 \qquad 1820-429 = 1391$

4. $240 \times 0.08 = 19 \qquad 32+19+6 = 57 \qquad 240 \times 0.08 = 19 \qquad 240-57 = 183$

Req. 2

pg. 445

		Journal					
DATE		ACCOUNTS AND EXPLANATIONS	POST. REF.	DEBIT		CREDIT	
Dec.	29	Salary Expense		3 0 9 3			
		Employee Federal Income Tax Payable				5 1 5	
		FICA Tax Payable				1 6 6	
		Employee Health Insurance Payable				7 8	
		Salary Payable				2 3 3 4	

Reqs. 3&4

		Journal					
DATE		ACCOUNTS AND EXPLANATIONS	POST. REF.	DEBIT		CREDIT	

Journal

DATE		ACCOUNTS AND EXPLANATIONS	POST. REF.	DEBIT	CREDIT
2005					
Jan.	9	Equipment		20000	
		Note Payable - Short-term			20000
Jan.	29	Cash (40,000 x $^{3}/_{4}$ = 30,000 x 1.06 = 31,800)			
		Accounts Receivable			
		Sales Revenue			40000
		Sales Taxes Payable			

Reqs. 1 & 2 (Continued)

ACCOUNT					ACCOUNT NO.	
					BALANCE	
DATE	ITEM	JRNL. REF.	DEBIT	CREDIT	DEBIT	CREDIT

ACCOUNT					ACCOUNT NO.	
					BALANCE	
DATE	ITEM	JRNL. REF.	DEBIT	CREDIT	DEBIT	CREDIT

ACCOUNT					ACCOUNT NO.	
					BALANCE	
DATE	ITEM	JRNL. REF.	DEBIT	CREDIT	DEBIT	CREDIT

ACCOUNT					ACCOUNT NO.	
					BALANCE	
DATE	ITEM	JRNL. REF.	DEBIT	CREDIT	DEBIT	CREDIT

Req. 2

		Journal			
DATE	ACCOUNTS AND EXPLANATIONS	POST. REF.	DEBIT	CREDIT

Reqs. 1&2

NAME
SECTION
DATE

Chapter 11

Decision Case 1
(Continued)

Reqs. 1&2 (Continued)

Reqs. 1–3

Req. 1

General Journal

DATE	ACCOUNTS AND EXPLANATIONS	POST. REF.	DEBIT	CREDIT

Req. 2

Req. 3

Req. 1

NAME
SECTION
DATE

Chapter 11

Team Project 1

(Continued)

Req. 2

NAME
SECTION
DATE

Chapter 11

Team Project 2

(Continued)

Reqs. 1–3

Reqs. 1 –3 (Continued)

Comprehensive Problem

Req. 1

Req. 2

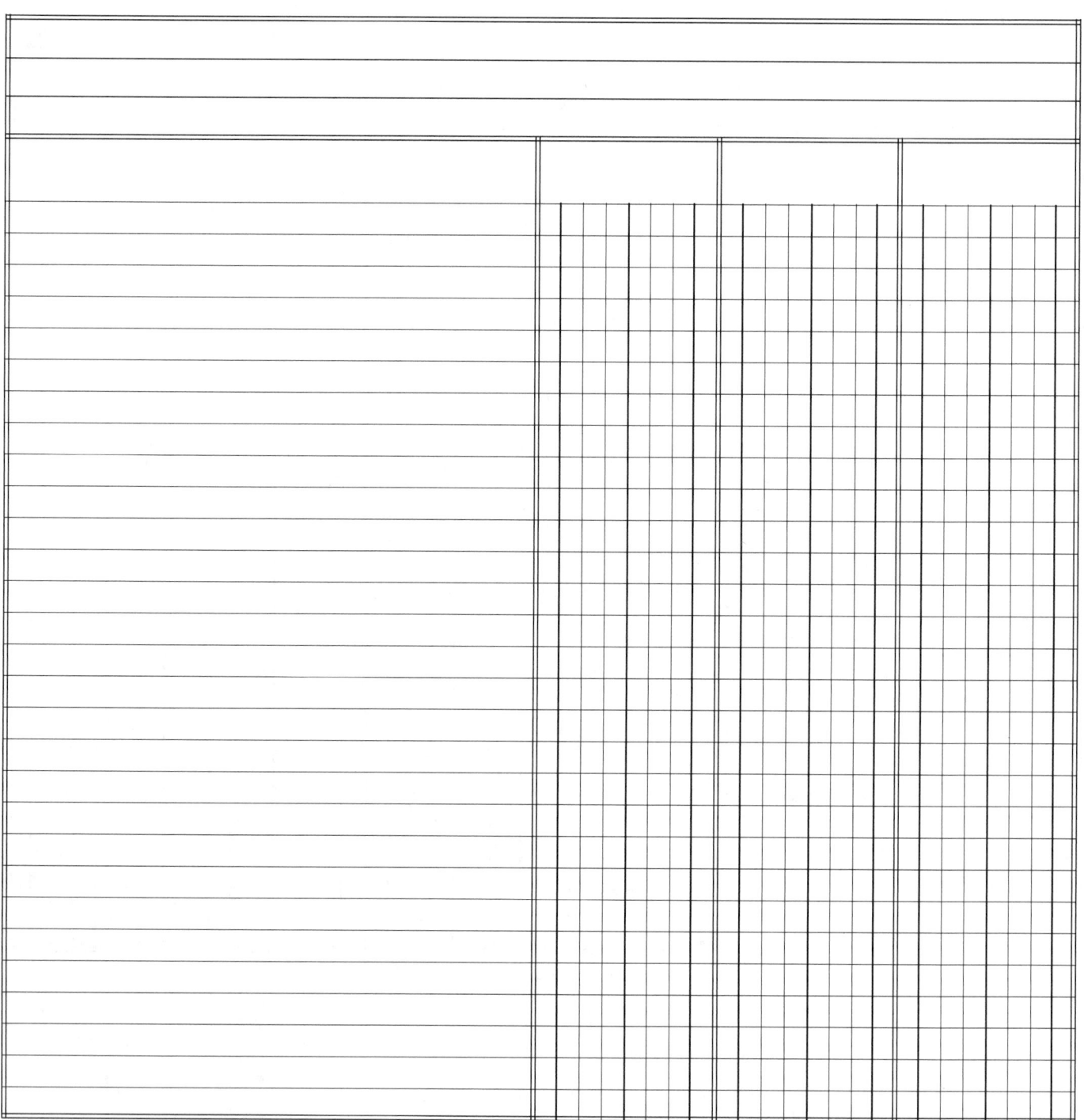

Req. 3

Req. 1

Req. 2

		Journal				
DATE		ACCOUNTS AND EXPLANATIONS	POST. REF.	DEBIT		CREDIT

Req. 1

_____

_____

_____

_____

_____

_____

Req. 2

		Journal			
DATE		ACCOUNTS AND EXPLANATIONS	POST. REF.	DEBIT	CREDIT

Req. 1

_____

_____

_____

_____

Req. 2

Req. 1

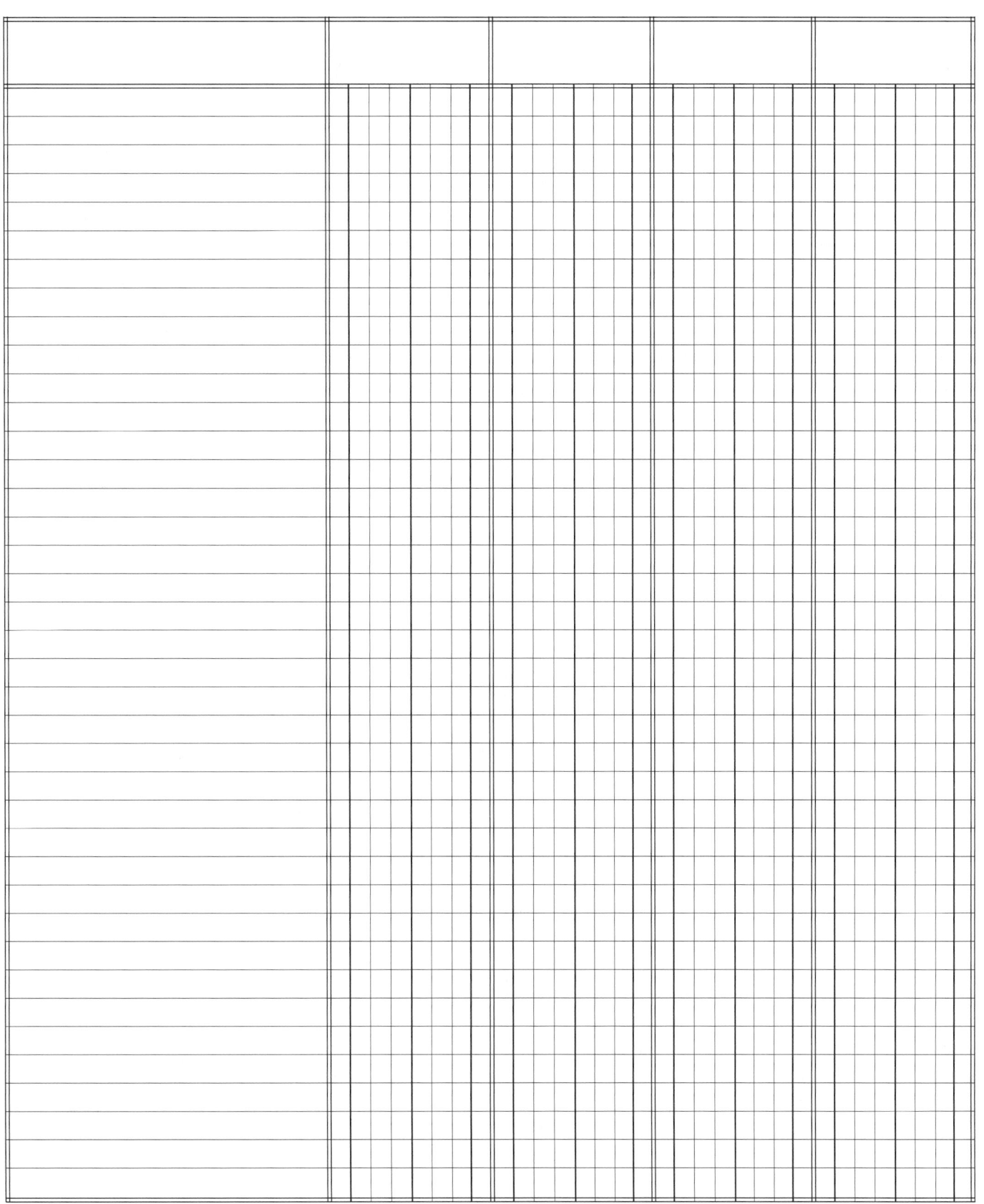

Req. 1

	Journal			
DATE	ACCOUNTS AND EXPLANATIONS	POST. REF.	DEBIT	CREDIT

Req. 2

Req. 1

S12-7

Req. 2

	Journal			
DATE	ACCOUNTS AND EXPLANATIONS	POST. REF.	DEBIT	CREDIT

Journal

DATE	ACCOUNTS AND EXPLANATIONS	POST. REF.	DEBIT	CREDIT

S12-9

	Journal				
DATE	ACCOUNTS AND EXPLANATIONS	POST. REF.	DEBIT	CREDIT

NAME
SECTION
DATE

CAPITAL

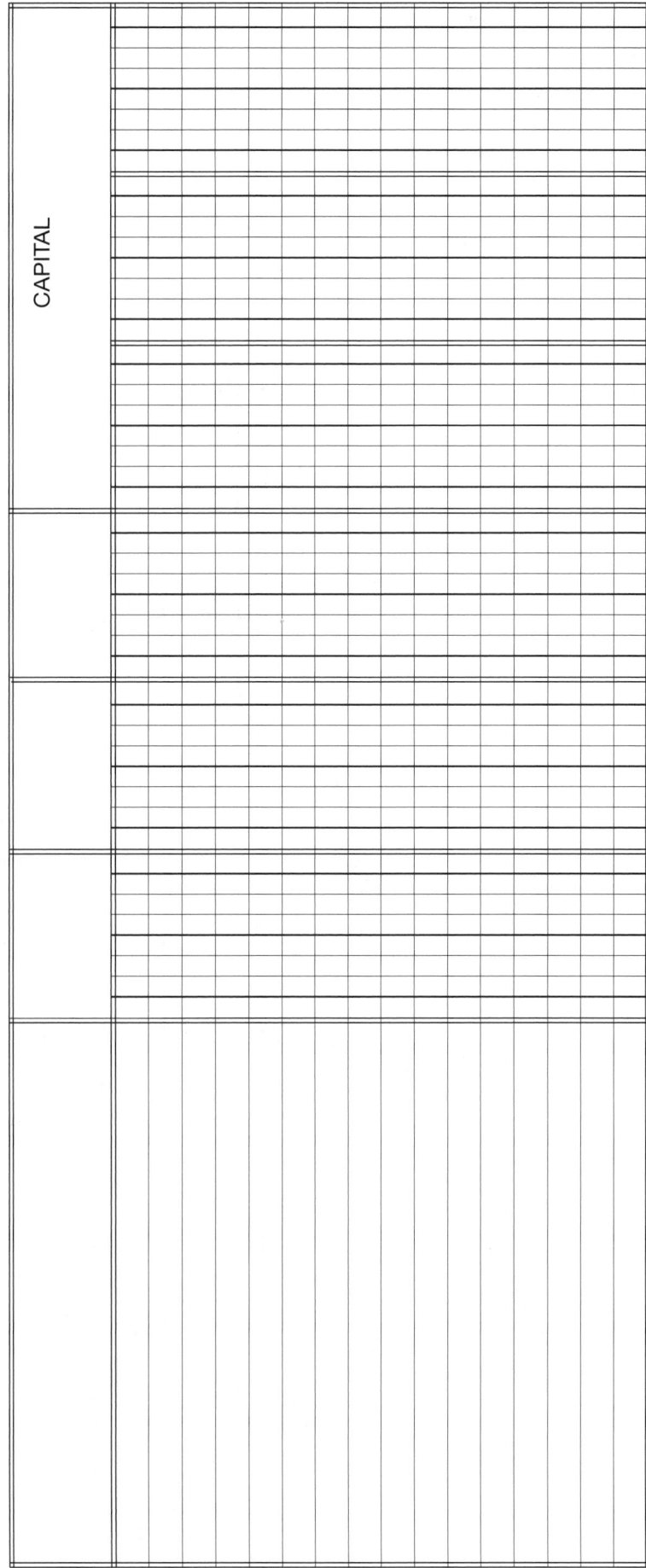

Journal

DATE	ACCOUNTS AND EXPLANATIONS	POST. REF.	DEBIT	CREDIT

S12-14

_____

_____

_____

_____

_____

_____

E12-2

		Journal			
DATE		ACCOUNTS AND EXPLANATIONS	POST. REF.	DEBIT	CREDIT

Journal

DATE	ACCOUNTS AND EXPLANATIONS	POST. REF.	DEBIT	CREDIT

Journal

DATE	ACCOUNTS AND EXPLANATIONS	POST. REF.	DEBIT	CREDIT

Journal

DATE	ACCOUNTS AND EXPLANATIONS	POST. REF.	DEBIT	CREDIT

Req. 1

Req. 2

E12-10

NAME
SECTION
DATE

		CAPITAL	

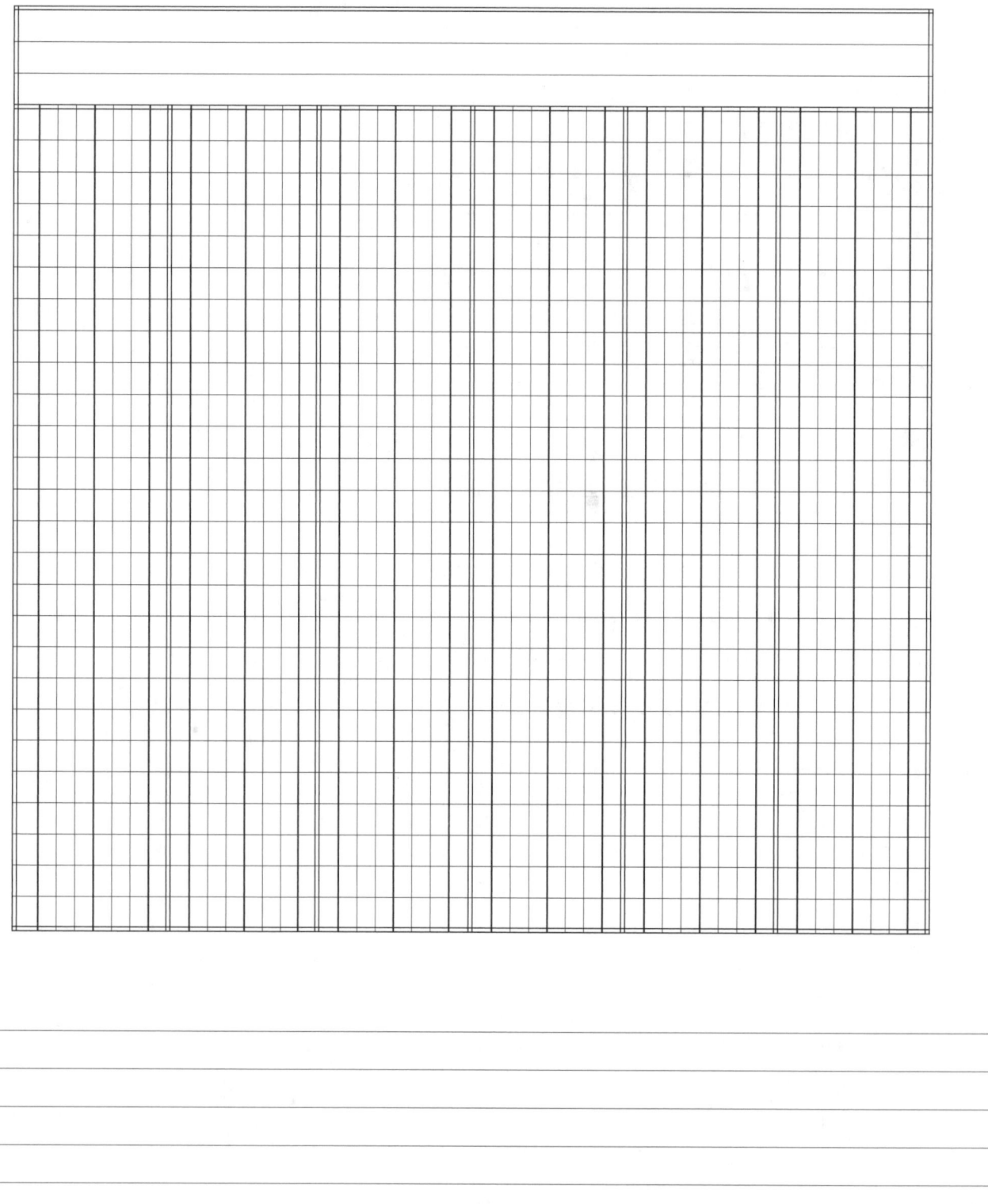

Reqs. 1 & 3

		Journal																
DATE		ACCOUNTS AND EXPLANATIONS	POST. REF.		DEBIT						CREDIT							

Req. 2

Reqs. 1 & 2

	Journal				
DATE	ACCOUNTS AND EXPLANATIONS	POST. REF.	DEBIT		CREDIT

Req. 3

	Journal			
DATE	ACCOUNTS AND EXPLANATIONS	POST. REF.	DEBIT	CREDIT

NAME
SECTION
DATE

Req. 1

P12-4A

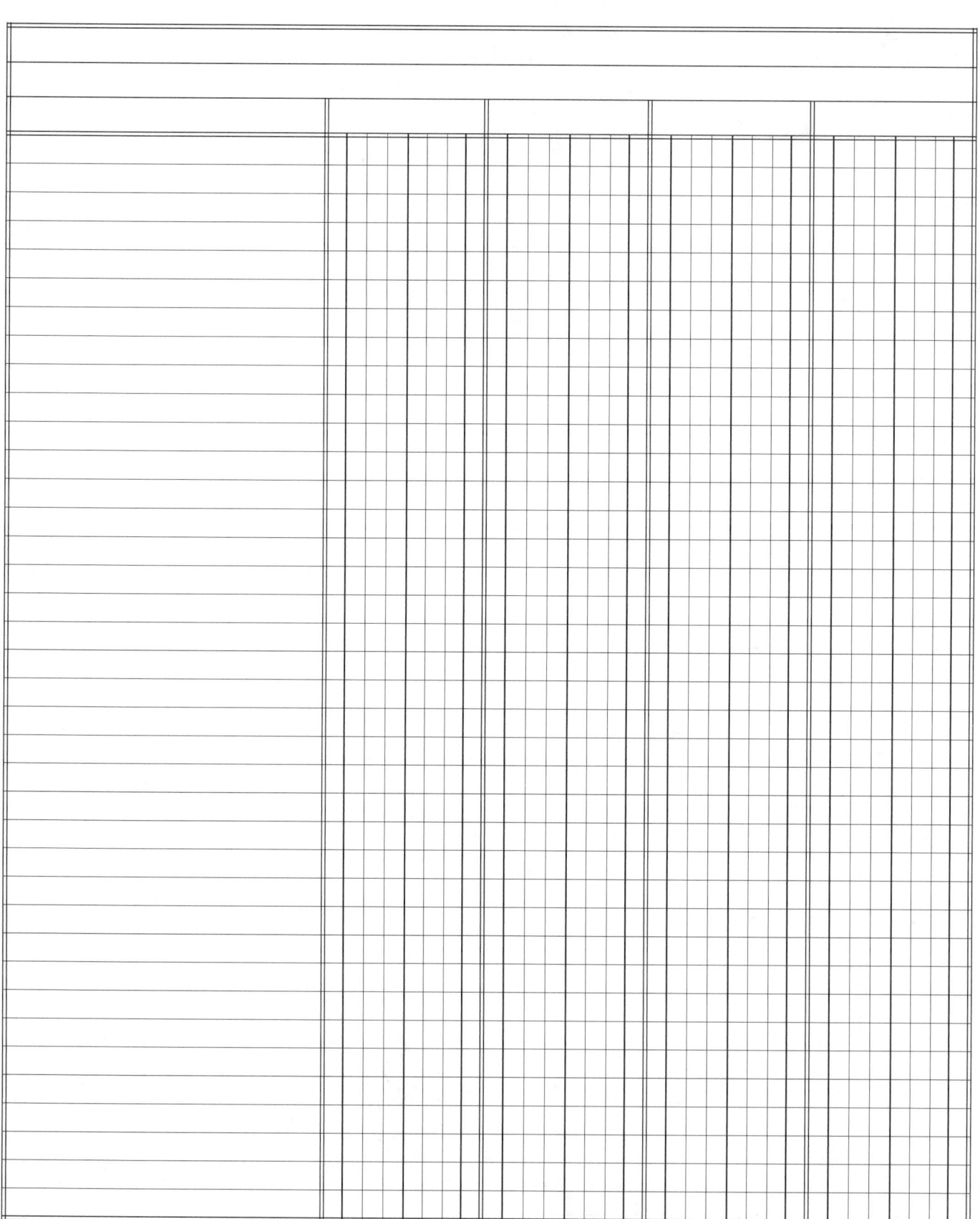

Req. 1 (Continued)

Req. 1 (Continued)

Req. 2

Reqs. 1–4

		Journal			
DATE		ACCOUNTS AND EXPLANATIONS	POST. REF.	DEBIT	CREDIT

Reqs. 1–4 (Continued)

		Journal			
DATE	ACCOUNTS AND EXPLANATIONS	POST. REF.	DEBIT	CREDIT	

NAME
SECTION
DATE

Req. 1

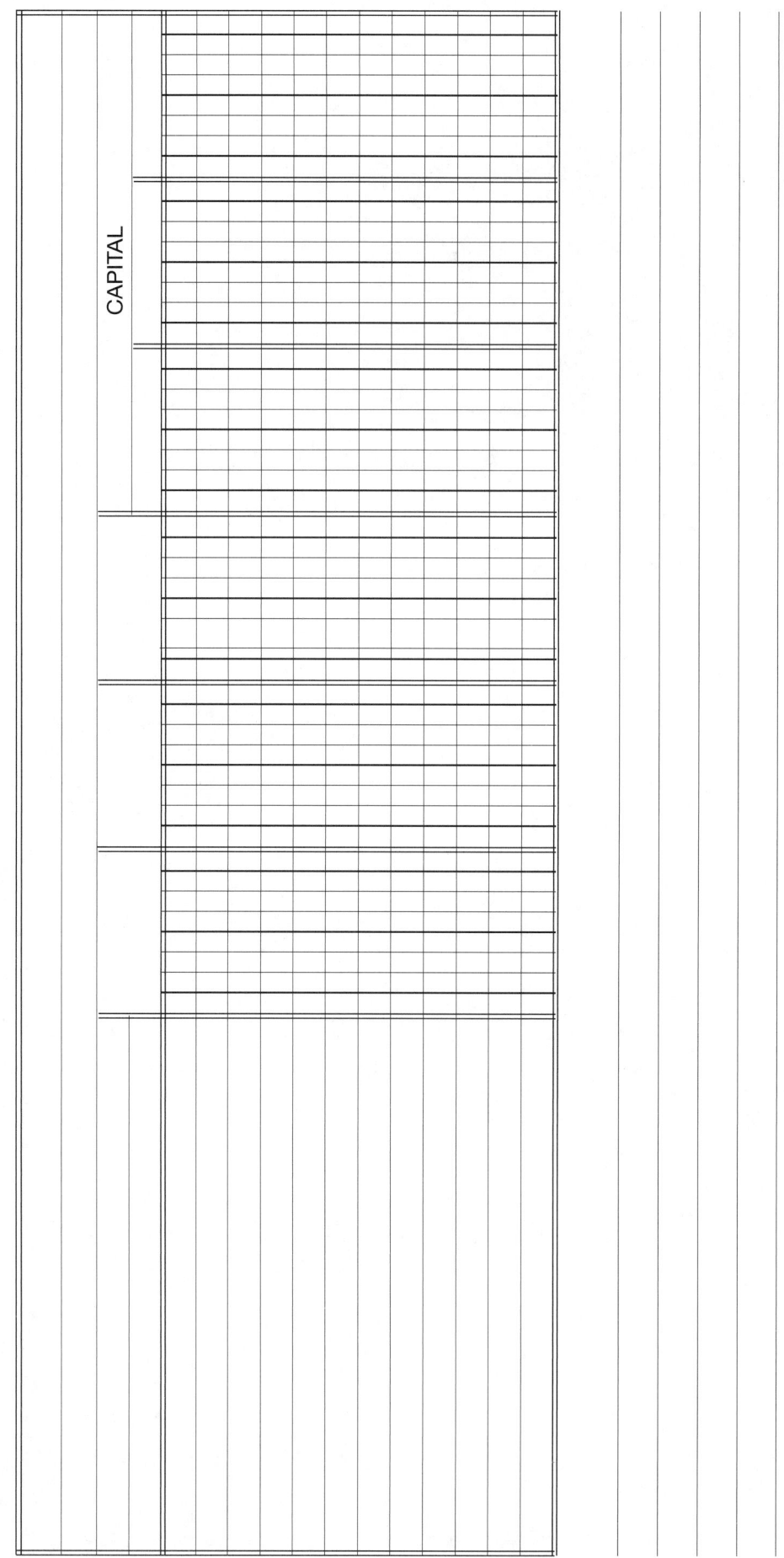

CAPITAL

Req. 2

		Journal				
DATE		ACCOUNTS AND EXPLANATIONS	POST. REF.	DEBIT		CREDIT

Req. 1

		Journal			
DATE	ACCOUNTS AND EXPLANATIONS	POST. REF.	DEBIT	CREDIT	

Req. 2

Reqs. 1 & 3

		Journal			
DATE		ACCOUNTS AND EXPLANATIONS	POST. REF.	DEBIT	CREDIT

Req. 2

Reqs. 1–3

	Journal				
DATE	ACCOUNTS AND EXPLANATIONS	POST. REF.	DEBIT	CREDIT	

Reqs. 1–3 (Continued)

	Journal					
DATE	ACCOUNTS AND EXPLANATIONS	POST. REF.	DEBIT		CREDIT	

Req. 1

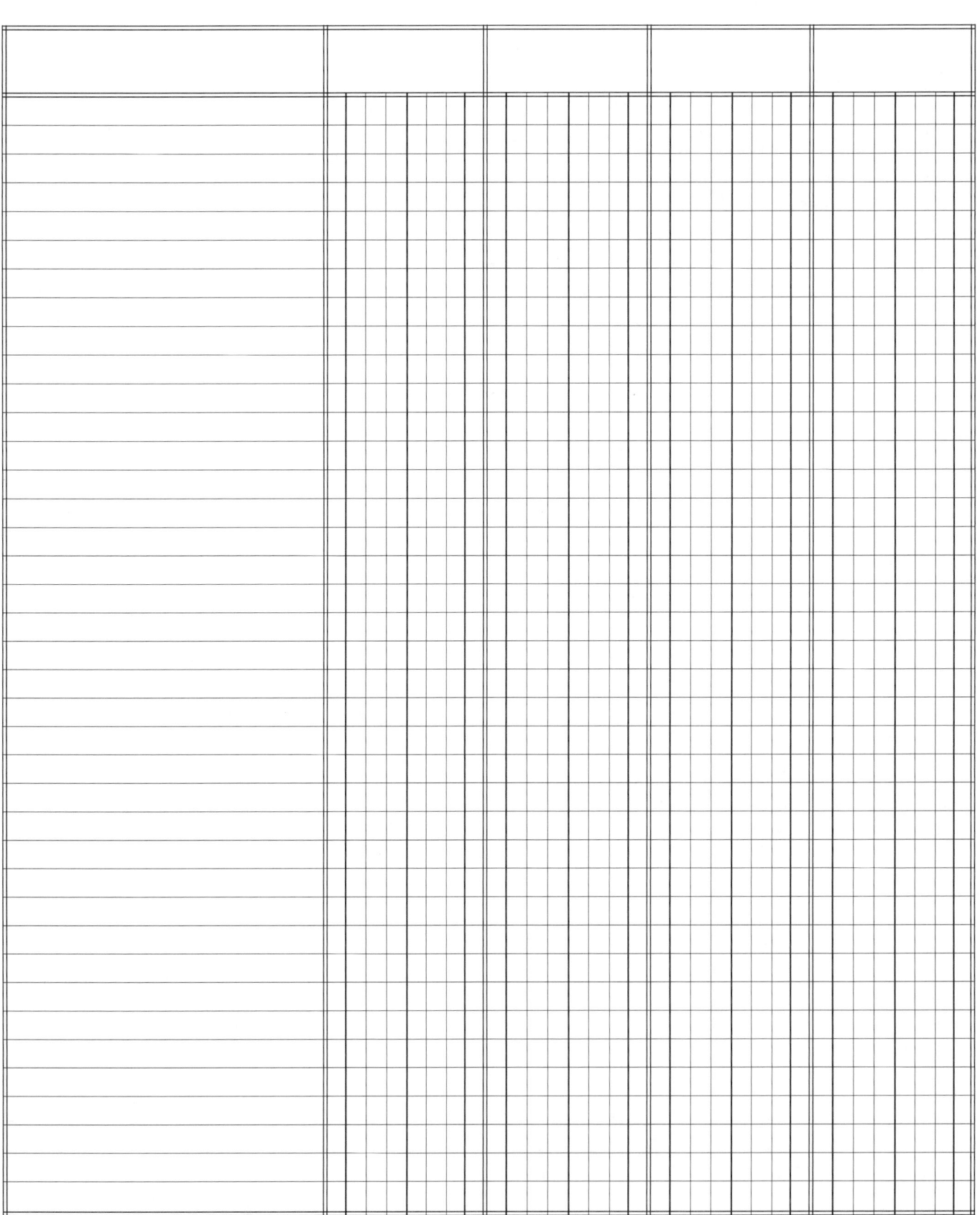

Req. 1 (Continued)

Req. 2

Reqs. 1–4

		Journal																		
DATE		ACCOUNTS AND EXPLANATIONS	POST. REF.		DEBIT							CREDIT					

Reqs. 1–4 (Continued)

		Journal			
DATE		ACCOUNTS AND EXPLANATIONS	POST. REF.	DEBIT	CREDIT

Chapter 12

NAME
SECTION
DATE

Req. 1

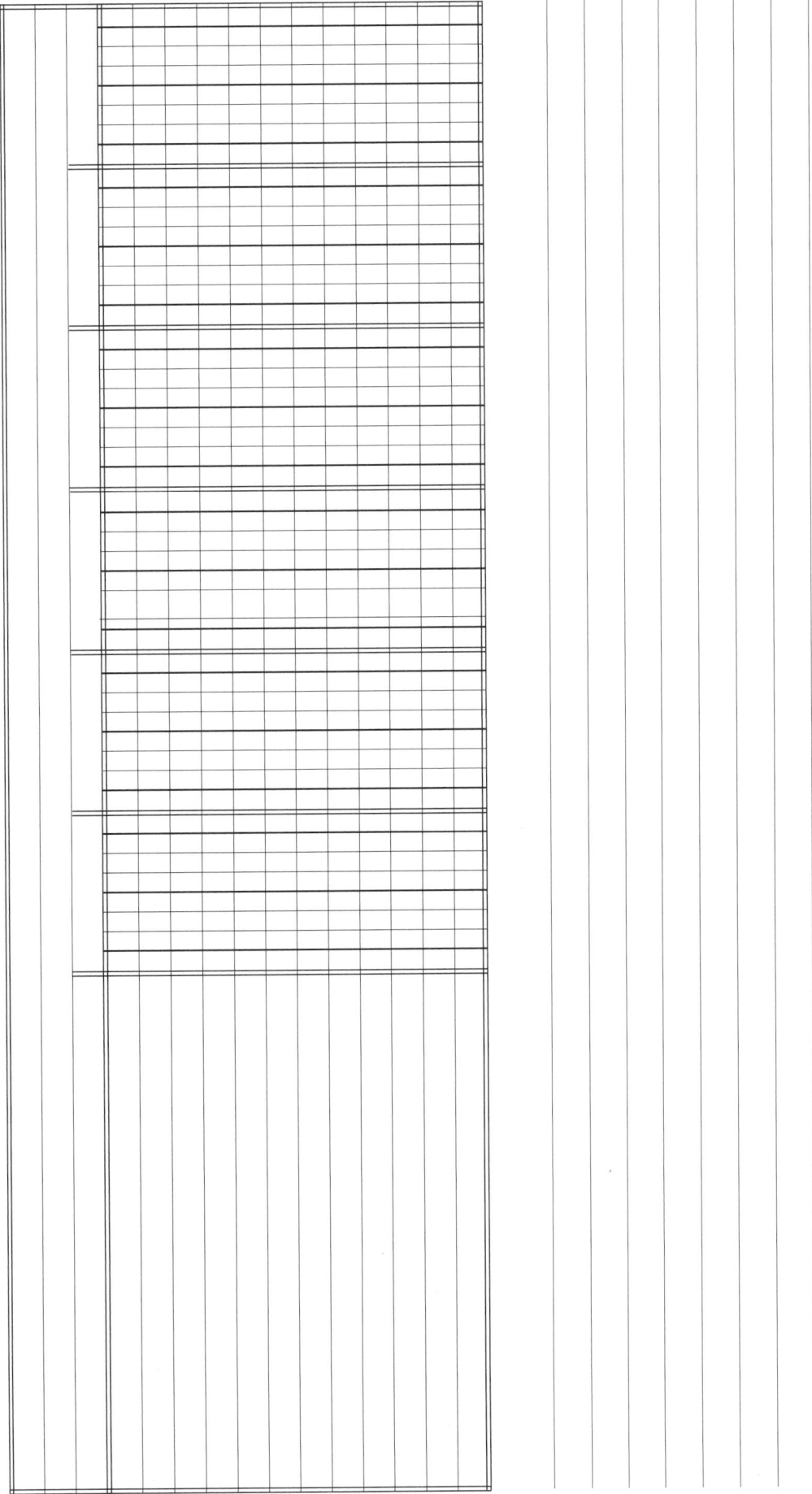

Req. 2

		Journal					
DATE		ACCOUNTS AND EXPLANATIONS	POST. REF.	DEBIT		CREDIT	

Req. 1

		Journal			
DATE		ACCOUNTS AND EXPLANATIONS	POST. REF.	DEBIT	CREDIT

Req. 2

NAME
SECTION
DATE

Chapter 12

Decision Case 2

Reqs. 1–3

Req. 1

	Journal			
DATE	ACCOUNTS AND EXPLANATIONS	POST. REF.	DEBIT	CREDIT

Req. 2

S13-2

Case A

Journal										
DATE		ACCOUNTS AND EXPLANATIONS	POST. REF.	DEBIT				CREDIT		

Case B

Journal										
DATE		ACCOUNTS AND EXPLANATIONS	POST. REF.	DEBIT				CREDIT		

Journal

DATE	ACCOUNTS AND EXPLANATIONS	POST. REF.	DEBIT	CREDIT

		Journal					
DATE		ACCOUNTS AND EXPLANATIONS	POST. REF.	DEBIT		CREDIT	

S13-8

		Journal			
DATE		ACCOUNTS AND EXPLANATIONS	POST. REF.	DEBIT	CREDIT

S13-12

Journal

DATE	ACCOUNTS AND EXPLANATIONS	POST. REF.	DEBIT	CREDIT

Req. 1

DATE		ACCOUNTS AND EXPLANATIONS	POST. REF.	DEBIT	CREDIT
		Journal			

Req. 2

Req. 1

Journal

DATE	ACCOUNTS AND EXPLANATIONS	POST. REF.	DEBIT	CREDIT

Req. 2

Journal

DATE	ACCOUNTS AND EXPLANATIONS	POST. REF.	DEBIT	CREDIT

E13-6

E13-11

Req. 1

		Journal	POST. REF.	DEBIT	CREDIT
DATE		ACCOUNTS AND EXPLANATIONS			

Req. 2

Journal

DATE	ACCOUNTS AND EXPLANATIONS	POST. REF.	DEBIT	CREDIT

Req. 1

		Journal	POST. REF.	DEBIT	CREDIT
DATE		ACCOUNTS AND EXPLANATIONS			

Req. 2

Stockholders' Equity	

Reqs. 1–3

Req. 4

		Journal			
DATE		ACCOUNTS AND EXPLANATIONS	POST. REF.	DEBIT	CREDIT

Req. 5

Req. 1

Req. 2

		Journal			
DATE		ACCOUNTS AND EXPLANATIONS	POST. REF.	DEBIT	CREDIT

Req. 3

	Journal			
DATE	ACCOUNTS AND EXPLANATIONS	POST. REF.	DEBIT	CREDIT

Req. 1

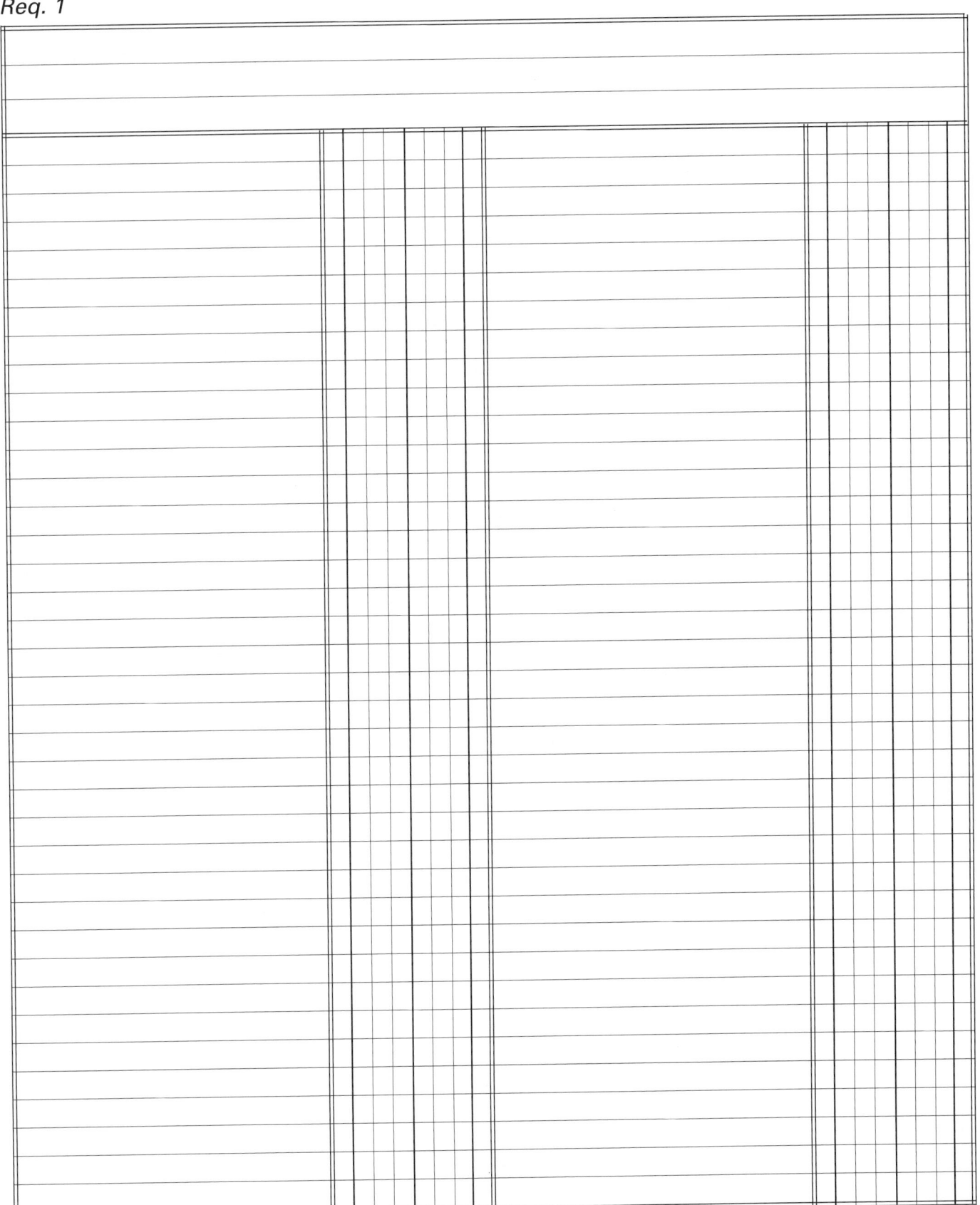

Reqs. 2 & 3

Req. 1a

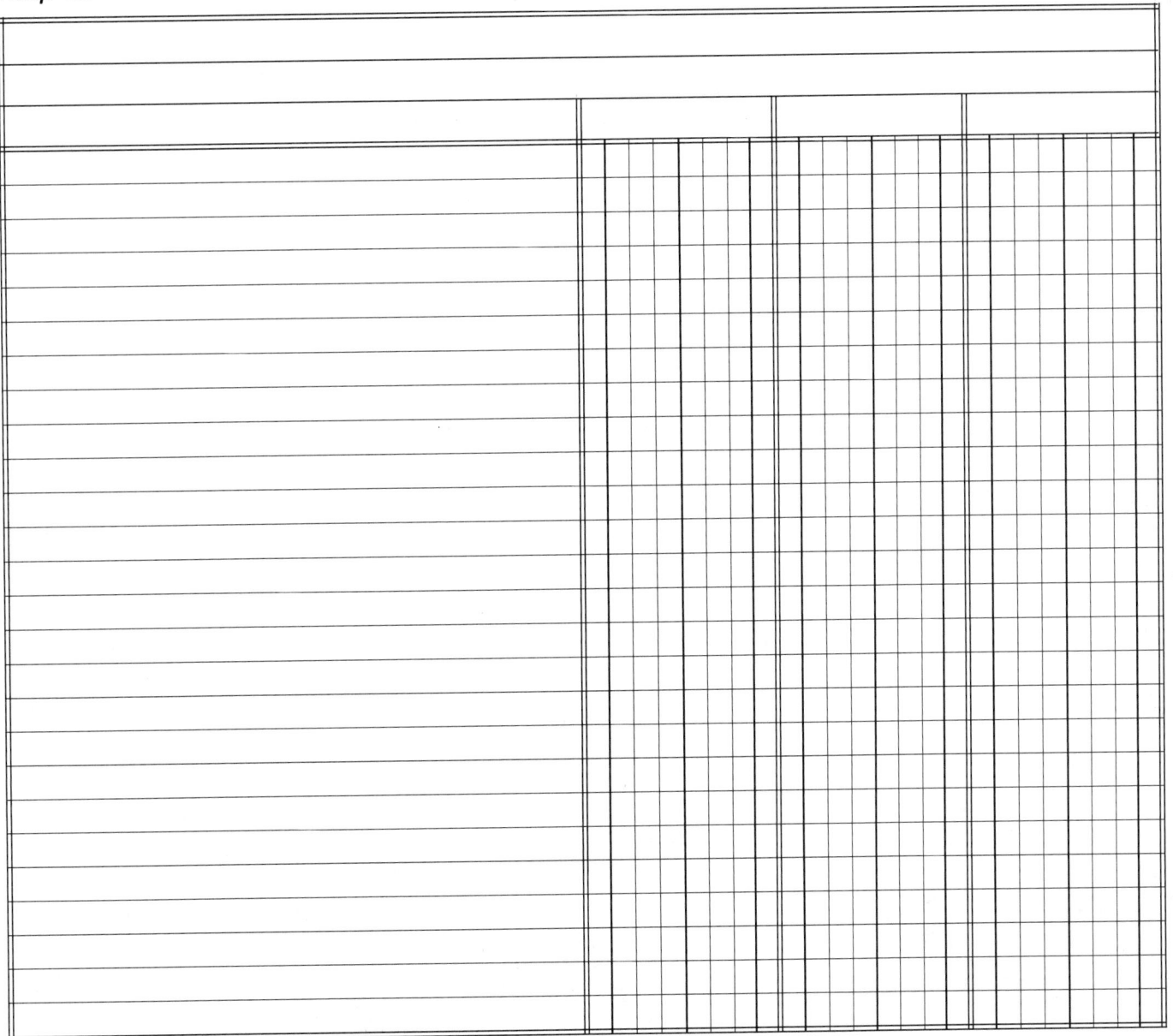

Req. 1b

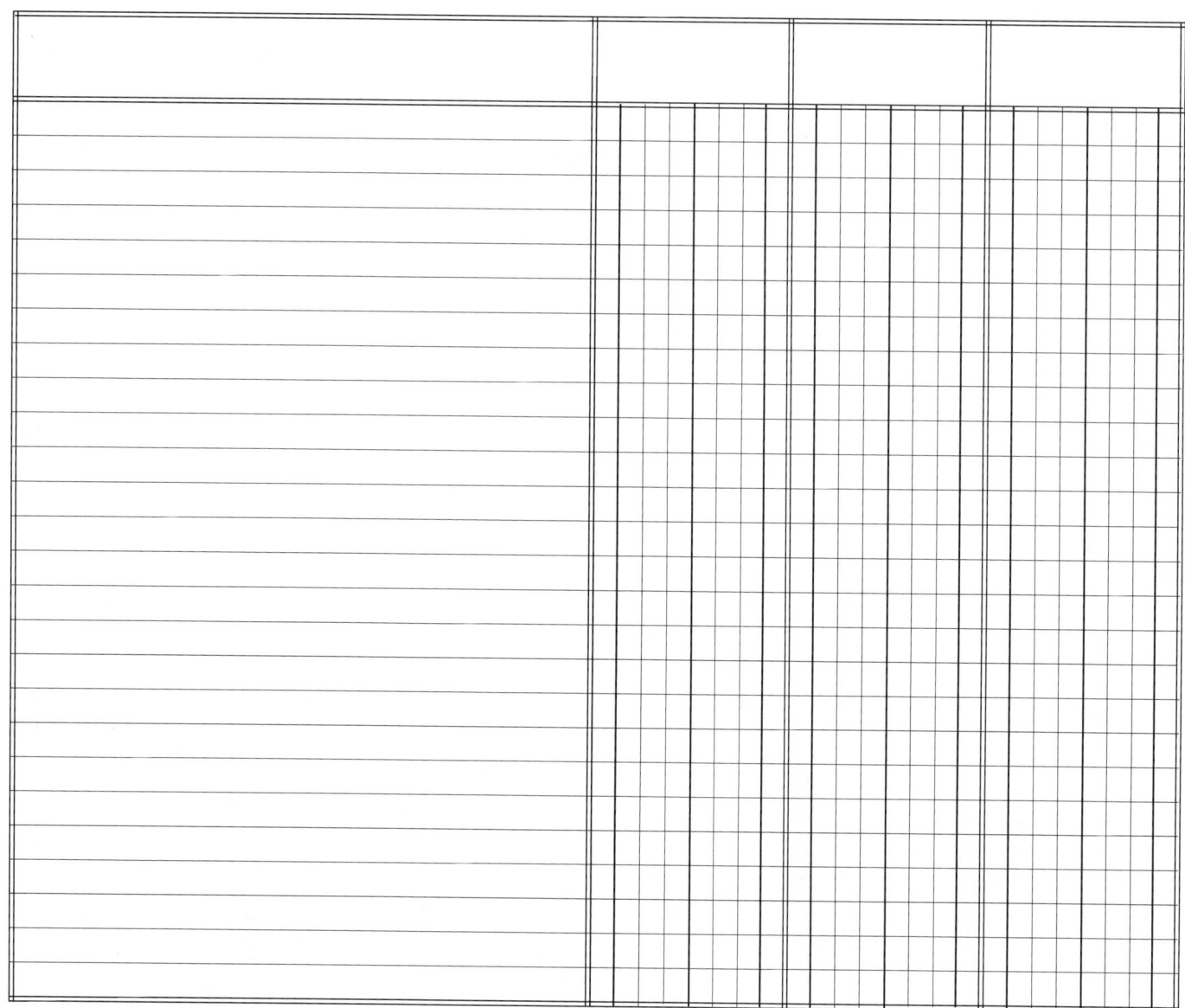

Req. 2

		Journal				
DATE		ACCOUNTS AND EXPLANATIONS	POST. REF.	DEBIT		CREDIT

Reqs. 1–5

Req. 6

Req. 1

Req. 2

		Journal			
DATE		ACCOUNTS AND EXPLANATIONS	POST. REF.	DEBIT	CREDIT

Req. 3

Req. 1

		Journal				
DATE		ACCOUNTS AND EXPLANATIONS	POST. REF.	DEBIT		CREDIT

Req. 2

Req. 1–3

Req. 4

		Journal			
DATE		ACCOUNTS AND EXPLANATIONS	POST. REF.	DEBIT	CREDIT

Req. 5

Computation:

Computation:

Req. 1

_____

_____

_____

_____

Req. 2

		Journal			
DATE		ACCOUNTS AND EXPLANATIONS	POST. REF.	DEBIT	CREDIT

Req. 3

		Journal			
DATE		ACCOUNTS AND EXPLANATIONS	POST. REF.	DEBIT	CREDIT

Req. 1

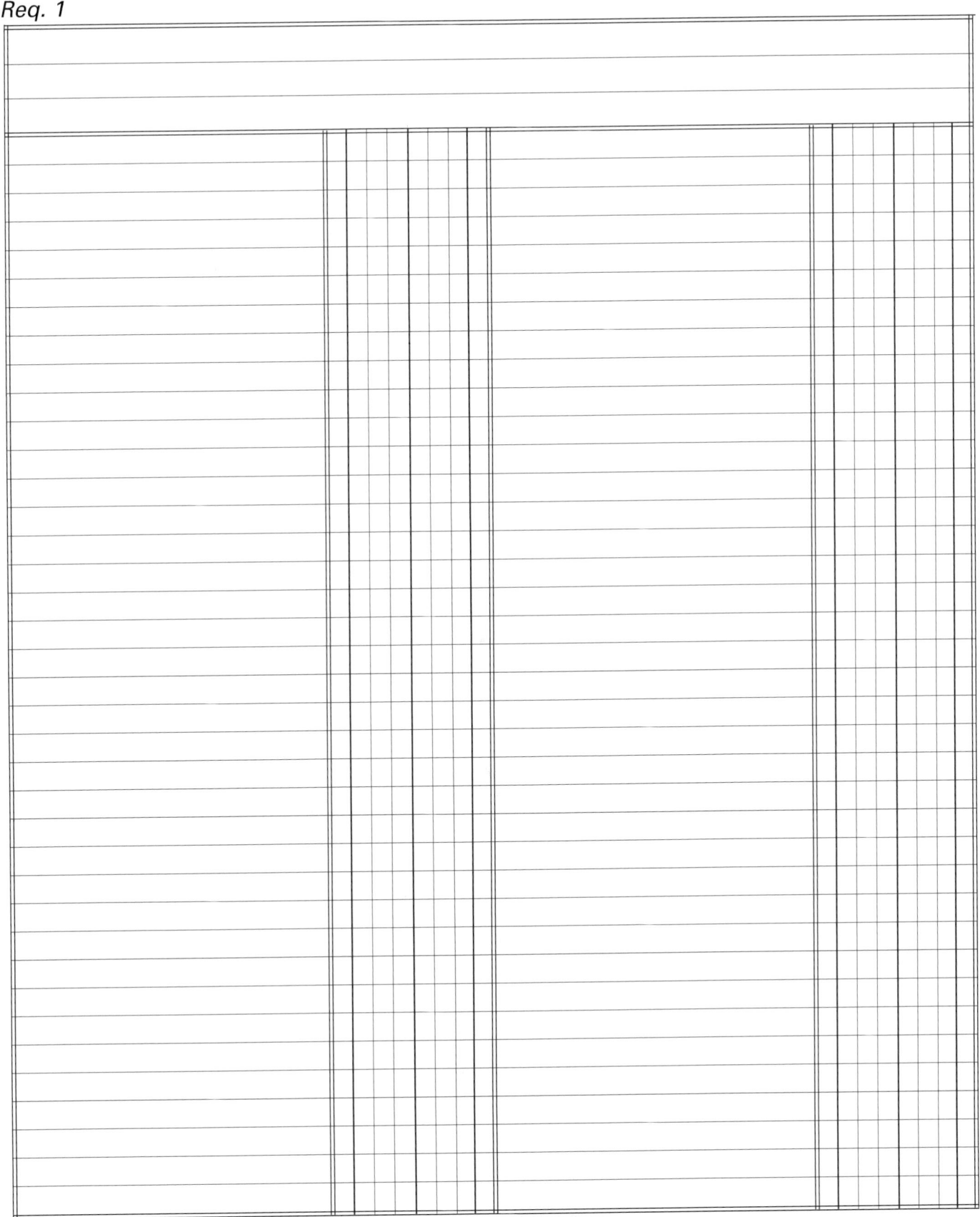

Reqs. 2 & 3

Req. 1a

Req. 1b

Req. 2

		Journal			
DATE		ACCOUNTS AND EXPLANATIONS	POST. REF.	DEBIT	CREDIT

Req. 1–4

Req. 5

Req. 1

Req. 2

Journal

DATE	ACCOUNTS AND EXPLANATIONS	POST. REF.	DEBIT	CREDIT

Req. 3

Reqs. 1 & 2

	Journal			
DATE	ACCOUNTS AND EXPLANATIONS	POST. REF.	DEBIT	CREDIT

NAME
SECTION
DATE

Chapter 13

Decision Case 1
(Continued)

Req. 3

Plan 1:

Plan 2:

NAME
SECTION
DATE

Chapter 13

Decision Case 1
(Continued)

Req. 4

Reqs. 1–4

Reqs. 1 & 2

NAME
SECTION
DATE

Chapter 13

Financial
Statement Case

Reqs. 1–4

Reqs. 1–3

NAME

SECTION

DATE

Chapter 13

Team Project

(Continued)

Reqs. 1–3 (continued)

NAME
SECTION
DATE

Chapter 13

Team Project
(Continued)

Reqs. 1–3 (continued)